I MARRIED JOAN

Joan Park

ISIS

LARGE PRINT

Oxford

First published in Great Britain 2005
by Isis Publishing Ltd.

Published in Large Print 2005 by ISIS Publishing Ltd,
7 Centremead, Osney Mead, Oxford OX2 0ES
by arrangement with the author

British Library Cataloguing in Publication Data
Park, Joan
    I married Joan. – Large print ed.
    (Isis reminiscence series)
    1. Park, Joan 2. Women teachers – Scotland –
    Glasgow – Biography
    3. Teachers – Scotland – Glasgow – Biography
    4. Teachers' spouses – Scotland – Glasgow –
    Biography 5. Husbands – Effects of wife's employ-
    ment on – Scotland – Glasgow 6. Marriage
    7. Large type books
    I. Title
    941.4'4085'092

ISBN 0–7531–9988–2 (hb)
ISBN 0–7531–9989–0 (pb)

Printed and bound by Antony Rowe, Chippenham

*To my daughter and son who, with me
shared most of these forty years.*

I wish to thank the editorial staff at Isis for their faithful support, my daughter who corrected what I thought was the final script, my friend Lesley McTaggart who helped me to correct copy and my son who continues to supply me with computer tools and skills.

Introduction

Until recently I had been sure that the person who was required to exercise the most tolerance in our marriage was me.

I fell in love with and, in 1953, married a man eleven years my senior. In writing about our forty years of marriage I have used the voice of my husband to reflect the viewpoint of the post-war male.

Alex Park was just one of a generation of men who expected a wife to fit into the role model he had in mind. To the extent that he had conformed to the wishes of his parents, he anticipated that his children would do likewise. It is understandable that despite his good intentions he was to encounter much that to him was incomprehensible and frustrating. Within this framework can be found both the humour and the sadness.

By describing the years 1953 to 1993 as he possibly saw them, I have tried to show that he, rather than me, was responsible for most of the input of love and acceptance which enabled us to survive as a close family.

CHAPTER
ONE

"What kind of a wife do you think Joan would make?" This is the question I ask of Bob, half in fun, half in earnest. It is 1952 and Bob and I are having our regular Sunday afternoon stroll which will end with us sitting in the local café drinking cokes or eating ice cream. It is early September and about a month since we returned from our summer holiday in Morecambe. In five summers this was the third summer holiday we had spent with Joan and her sister, Thelma.

I'm an old bachelor of 39 and Bob is older than that but he was married soon after the end of the war. His marriage didn't last and that was mostly Bob's fault. Bob is a reformed character now but at the time he was drinking heavily. His idea of a good time was to invite his drinking pals round to his house every night to play cards until the early hours of the morning. No wife is going to put up with that for long and Bob's wife was no exception, so it all ended in divorce. I don't drink and never have done. That's not for any noble reason. I just think it's a waste of money as far as I'm concerned in that I've never found any alcoholic drink that I like. Given the choice I stick to coke and ginger beer.

Bob and I worked on the Pullman dining cars together. We shared an uncle who got us the jobs soon after leaving school. That's where we met Tom, who was a chef on the cars. We regularly play bridge with Tom and his wife, Annie. They live in the sandstone tenement buildings in Calder Street in Govanhill on the south side of Glasgow. Their house is opposite the public baths, just a five-minute walk away from where I live with my sister, Maisie, and her two little girls in a council house. We were allowed to stay there after my father died. My younger brothers left during the war years and they are married with children. Except for meeting up with Bob to play cards or take a Sunday afternoon outing I don't see much of him these days. He has become very friendly with Isabel who is a different type from his first wife. I have to say she's a bit too prim and proper for me but she'll keep Bob on the straight and narrow. They are planning to marry next March.

So, you see, Bob had to be a bit close about going away in the summer with me. I don't imagine that he told Isabel that he intended seeing Thelma throughout the holiday. More likely he made out he was going the holiday with me because it had been arranged since last summer and he couldn't let me down. This was true but not the whole truth, which was that we both enjoyed the company of Thelma and her younger sister, Joan. The three holidays we had spent together were quite the best since those pre-war holidays in Jersey and both Bob and I were sorry to see them end. We had told the girls it was the last holiday we could have as a foursome. Bob said that Thelma wasn't too put out. After all, there was another Bob in her life, even though it seemed he just met with her when it was convenient for him. We doubted anything would come of it marriage-wise.

I know it is different for Joan. I know we get on well together and we both want to find a way for it to continue. I just cannot see how. After all, I live in Glasgow and she is over two hundred miles away in Liverpool. I get one two-week holiday at the Glasgow Fair and, as an inspector in Simpson and Shaw, I even work Saturdays. There's no chance of meeting halfway for a long weekend and there is no way I am going to drive eighty miles to Carlisle or the Lakes on a Saturday evening to leave again 24 hours later. It just isn't on. I cannot really see the point of continuing the correspondence that has been going on since we first met in 1947, but Joan obviously wants to and perhaps I find it easier to open up in a letter than I do when I'm with her. Unlike her I don't exactly wear my heart on my sleeve. Yet in a way it is because she doesn't act coy or play hard to get like many other girls I've met that I find her attractive.

Heaven only knows what she finds attractive in me. I'm even losing my top hair. It is very flattering to me to think that approaching forty and with eleven years of a difference in our ages I can still find someone who enjoys my company, laughs at my jokes and is impressed by my performance on a dance floor and the less than remarkable skill of knowing the lyrics of all the dance band numbers. That's hardly a basis for marriage, is it? I tell her that I am a different person on holiday from what I am at home in Glasgow and that she really doesn't know me at all. On the other hand, how do I explain that over the last month I'm finding it hard to settle down. There's times when I can't eat and there's times when I can't sleep. It is all quite ridiculous as I am telling Bob at this moment when I ask, "What kind of a wife do you think Joan would make?"

"Probably pretty awful," is Bob's reply with a grin. "I'll bet she's never cooked in her life. You'd be the guinea-pig for her to practise on. It would be a short life but a merry one. Are you prepared for that?"

I show Bob the two little books Joan sent to me. Each page has her own cartoon sketch of some memorable moment in the holidays. Below each sketch she has added her own comment. They cause us both to recall the occasions and laugh. "See what I mean," Bob says, "anyone who can spend so much time creating two books full of matchstick men must be living on a mushroom, but that's not saying she couldn't add a bit of spice to your solitary existence."

Towards the end of September I receive Joan's latest letter. She has had an idea. Why doesn't she come up and stay in Glasgow for her October holiday week? Joan teaches in primary school and unlike me gets loads of holidays. "That way," she writes, "it would give us a week together to make up our minds." I know Joan well enough to appreciate what it has cost her in pride to take the initiative and make this suggestion. I write back immediately to commend the idea. I busy myself booking her in for bed and breakfast at the Park Hotel,

4

a stone's throw from Calder Street. I have to put up with a bit of stick from Maisie who wants to know why Joan cannot stay with us.

"You could sleep in the living room," she says. "That way she could have your room." Maisie is obviously fearing that for some reason I think our house is not good enough. On the other hand I know that there's nothing Maisie would like better than to see me married and away, especially now that her husband, Fred, is no longer serving in the Navy and finds my presence in the house a bit of a pain. I could afford to live elsewhere but it helps Maisie out if I share the rent and the housekeeping, cash she would be too proud to take if I wasn't living with her.

"I'm only booking her in for bed and breakfast," I say, "we'll be eating out most nights. You can ask her for the odd lunch if you like."

"Maybe you'll want to vet the menu first," Maisie says with a sniff. "God forbid it should fall short of the standard she's used to."

Joan arrives by train on the Friday evening. I meet her and after we have deposited the suitcase at the hotel we drive out to Ayr for a meal. It is pouring with rain so back in the Riley after dinner I say, "I don't see the sense of wasting a whole week. I'm pretty sure you are not going to say no to becoming engaged tonight and having the week for all my friends and family to meet you."

Joan says, "I thought we were supposed to spend the week finding out if we are suited to one another."

5

I laugh outright. "What could we possibly find out in a week that we don't know already? I've arranged to be out on inspection with Mrs. Cook next week. She's my best traveller and we'll be finished each day by lunchtime. You and I will have lots of time together. I've to work tomorrow morning but you can go into town and I'll meet you at lunchtime to choose the ring. What I would really like is to invite about twelve people to our engagement party in the Plaza ballroom. On a Thursday evening they have special arrangements for private parties. You'll love it."

We do just as I have planned for the whole week. I trot Joan round to meet Annie, who works in a gent's outfitters under the railway bridge in Argyle Street. Annie invites us round to a meal. We spend Sunday driving round Loch Lomond, except you can see nothing for the pouring rain. I take my war photograph albums in the car and we park at the loch side while I talk her through the albums. The photographs cover my time ashore in Capetown, the Arctic convoys, the aircraft carriers in the Pacific when we worked alongside the Yanks, the American family who treated me like a son. I had a good war.

On the Sunday evening Neil comes to pick us up on his way to church. He is quite horrified that Joan is prepared to go to church hatless.

"I'm sure Maisie will lend you one of hers," he says.

Joan laughs, "I always go to church without a hat."

"Possibly," Neil says, "but that is the Church of England. This is a Baptist church. I don't want you to feel embarrassed when all the other ladies will be wearing hats."

"I won't," says Joan.

Maisie, in the background, is struggling to hide her smile and secretly we are both enjoying the fact that Neil has met his match. Joan doesn't give a toss what other people think or do. By contrast, he is so conventional that he regularly goes to his office wearing a bowler hat and carrying a rolled-up umbrella.

Neil has been my pal since schooldays. I see more of him than I do Bob McAllister. We go to the cinema together a couple of times a week and I know he considers himself quite a man for the ladies. I would never go on holiday with him because although we are both members of the same golf club, I wouldn't put a round of golf as a priority for every day of the holiday as he would. I tell Joan she will see Neil at his most charming at the Plaza party. I say she might have second thoughts and decide he is the more eligible bachelor.

Joan says, "I'm a bit wary of being weighed up and found wanting by your friends."

"Oh, you don't need to worry on that score. For a start you've already met Tom and Annie and Maisie and Fred. You even met the Andersons last year in Southport. You know Bob, and he will bring Isabel as his partner. It will be Isabel everybody is weighing up. They can't wait to see who it is that is prepared to marry Bob."

The rest of the week flies by. Sitting in the cinema with the lights down, Joan finds it difficult not to stretch out her hand towards the darkest spot near the floor where she can best see the diamond flashing. It seems to me that most girls might have looked in a few shop windows and have known in advance what kind of ring they would like. Not so Joan. She looked in one window, liked the solitaire diamond in the platinum setting and we went into the shop and bought it.

The last day of Joan's October holiday arrives and I voice my fears. "Well, honey, here we are engaged yet I'm blessed if I know what happens next. How long do we wait until I even see you again? I suppose I have to start looking for a house. I have enough money to put down as a deposit to secure a mortgage on a new house. As the eldest I could stay in the Calder Street house, but Fred and Maisie haven't had much luck and I want them to keep it."

Joan says, "Why don't I go into the Education offices here in Bath Street and find out what I have to do to get a teaching job in Glasgow?"

Her new yellow raincoat is a little the worse for a week of rain and Glasgow soot but confidently she approaches the desk. In answer to her enquiry about school vacancies, the man behind the desk asks, "For cleaners?" When she makes it clear she is asking about vacancies for primary teachers she is told, "Oh, yes. If you work a three-month's notice in Liverpool and fill in this application form you can hope to start here in February".

We have already decided to get married in March. Neither of us would choose to have a big, expensive wedding. It will be at Joan's church in Liverpool and her mother will do the catering in their own home. If Joan had been the kind to stick out for a honeymoon we would have to wait until the Glasgow Fair next July for me to get away from the office. I tell her that tax-wise March is the better time. Joan returns to Liverpool and our correspondence continues. I don't find the house-hunting easy. Most of my friends are on the south side of Glasgow so naturally I'm looking in that area. I fancy a bungalow but they cost the earth. Re-building in the form of new houses hasn't really got going again since the war. I write to tell Joan that I need her here. I can't do the choosing on my own.

As it turns out, her interview for the teaching job is fixed for Christmas Eve, so I suggest that she stay up in Glasgow until the job starts. This will give us time to find a house and meantime could she please send me a photograph. I'm beginning to forget what she looks like.

I send Joan the cash to treat herself to a full-length evening dress for the Christmas dances we will be attending. I choose a bracelet watch for her Christmas present.

When I suggested that we only have a short engagement, she said she really needed some time to save as she had no savings. I said, "That isn't necessary, I've got plenty", but so that she doesn't feel entirely dependent on me I've since proposed that she cash in a stupid insurance policy that she has. I'm not against insurance. I worked for an insurance firm after the war. It is a way of saving money for people who can't save it any other way. I've always been in jobs that were pretty well paid and I've always been able to bank some of my wages. I'd reached the stage when I had begun to wonder if the cash was going to lie there until I died. To be sure. I don't economise on clothes and I bought the Riley. I bought it second-hand and I had it when we met for the second holiday, but it has cost me a fortune in repairs and replacements. I won't be able to afford to keep it after we are married. It is too old to be worth anything and I won't be buying another car until I can manage to buy a new one.

I arrange to meet Joan after her Bath Street interview. She is dancing on air. She already knows that her application has been accepted for a teaching post. She tells me that the interview was a breeze. She says that apparently Glasgow is so short of teachers that all they wanted to ascertain was that she had two legs to stand on in front of a class and enough sense to get her to the nearest bus stop for the school.

Because she won't be working until the new term begins in February, Annie has arranged for her to stay with a Mrs Parker who takes in boarders in the flat one down from theirs in Calder Street, nice and handy for us to get together. Maisie insists that Joan sleep at our house tonight so that she can watch her six-year old, Kat, open her presents on Christmas morning. Joan is giving Kat a beautiful wooden toy grocer's shop which she played with when she was a little girl.

The shop arrived a month ago. Joan's dad was coming up by ship to the Ibrox dock. I picked him up there to transport the shop and cases full of books and other belongings which Joan wanted up here. Her dad is very easy-going. Tom and Annie came down to our house for the evening and he slept at their house overnight. Tom plied him with whisky in the late hours and possibly most of the next day. When I drove him back to his ship he was euphoric about Scottish hospitality, the wonderful people all treating him like a long-lost friend and calling him Gerry. With tears in his eyes he repeated again and again how wonderful it was that his daughter was going to marry a man held in such high regard by his friends. On and on he went as I tried to interrupt to tell him that this was as far as I could take the car without driving into the Clyde. It is my guess that, unlike Tom, Gerry is not used to drinking whisky.

As one of my Christmas presents Joan gives me a tie. I know it is an expensive tie in that she bought it at Austin Reed's, where everything costs an arm and a leg, but it is not the kind of tie I would choose for myself. I say, "Well, it's no use pretending, love, it is very unlikely that you will ever see me wearing it. I like to choose my own ties."

We spend New Year's Eve in the home of Annie and Tom, having a meal which Tom has cooked specially and waiting to see in the New Year. When we break up in the early hours of the morning, Joan has only to go down the stair to the spacious, fire-lit bedsit which Mrs Parker has vacated for her use. She finds Mrs Parker's party is still in full swing in that room. She is invited to join in but, being desperate for sleep, she goes back up the stair and spends the night in one of Annie's easy chairs.

It is New Year's Day when we take a ten-minute drive to an area called Braehead where McTaggart and Mickle are building a new housing estate. We walk round the empty show house, a five-apartment. I've told Joan that I don't see myself becoming a father at forty plus so a three-apartment would be adequate. We discover that every three-apartment has already been sold. We settle for a four-apartment instead of a five because Joan prefers the bigger kitchen in lieu of a dining room. We accept the house which is nearest to completion and available by the end of the month. In no time at all I am negotiating a mortgage, paying out lawyers' fees and feu duty and wondering what happened to that huge sum of money I thought was lying in the bank. The house is to cost just under £2000 plus the interest over the twenty years it will take me to pay it. I take it out under an insurance policy so that if anything happens to me the house would be Joan's.

I spoke to my bosses the other day and asked them what kind of a deal they would offer if I bought all the furniture, carpets, curtains etc. at Simpson and Shaw. They were very generous. We couldn't do better. I'm in the office but the various heads of departments know me well, not only on business terms but because for long enough I ran the firm's social club. They say I can bring Joan into their departments, introduce her and then disappear back to the office. They will guide her to the best buys and, once the choice is made, they will ring me to come down and vet it. They promise that I'll get the best of everything, their own discount on top of what the bosses have agreed. Joan says it will cost more to let them make the curtains and she could make them herself. I say, "Rubbish! Why should you spend time doing that when they are cutting down on all the prices."

The first Saturday that Joan visits Simpson and Shaw I suggest that she confine herself to choosing four curtain materials, for living room, two bedrooms and kitchen, carpeting for living room and our bedroom, and the linoleum we will require for the hall plus living room and bedroom surrounds. I make a time about an hour and a half later for her to meet me in the furniture department to choose a three-piece suite. There are other occasions when the heads of department suggest that she visit one of the many warehouses with whom they trade, in order to have more choice. She is given a customer card to present there. I have to provide the instructions on how to get there and Joan finds her own way to bus routes.

By now she is teaching through the week and has to make time for these visits after four o'clock or on Saturday mornings. She makes plenty of mistakes in planning the time it will take to complete these trips and sometimes I'm waiting as long as ten minutes at some pre-arranged rendezvous. When she asks, "Ten minutes or half an hour, what's that to get worked up about?" I reply, "I'll tell you why. I don't keep you hanging around because I think it would be the height of bad manners. It would demonstrate lack of consideration. It is as good as saying that one person's time is less valuable than another's. One of these days you won't find me waiting." I'll say this for her. She has not kept me waiting since.

When Joan was here in October, we spent an afternoon walking round the Ideal Home Exhibition in the Kelvin Hall. As we looked at items, there wasn't once that we agreed on the same choice. This worried her more than it did me.

Mr. Fulford, head of the furniture department, walks round with us the day we are choosing dining and bedroom suites. Joan chooses a Beith dining room suite, light oak with mahogany lined drawers and cupboards in the sideboard. It has a matte finish. I choose the bedroom suite which has two large wardrobes. I don't intend sharing a wardrobe with anyone. There's a kidney-shaped dressing table with a rounded front. The whole has a highly polished dark walnut veneer, all very swish and modern. Mr Fulford smiles and says, "Your future wife's taste is superior to yours, my lad. That dining room suite will be as good 50 years from now. You'll be lucky if the bedroom suite lasts half that time."

Joan and I are happy that we each got one of our own choice. Joan follows up the suggestion that she should go to a recommended wholesale warehouse for the bed and I haven't the time to go with her. When we meet after her trip, she admits she was pretty flummoxed when asked what length of bed she was looking for. To help her out the assistant asked her was her husband a tall man and when Joan answered "Not very tall", she ended up ordering a 5'10" bed. I may not be tall by her standards, but I am 5'11" so we had to ask Mr Fulford to ring up and change the order.

We now have the keys to our new home so we go up there most evenings and at weekends. It is pretty cold, with unheated empty rooms, but we use an oil stove and we boil a kettle on top of it. We even boil eggs in the kettle. We sit on the floor, picnicking off heavy green Pyrex plates because we are waiting to see what wedding presents we are to be given before buying china. In several of these sessions I am putting up Harrison curtain rails at all the windows and laying linoleum surrounds in the main rooms. I get a great kick out of doing all these jobs and it's nice to have Joan chatting away, handing me tools and admiring my efforts. One night I am working away with the lino knife doing a mitred join at the corner. This is when Joan says, "Watch out, you're about to make that cut in the wrong direction."

I really can't believe my ears. Is she trying to tell me what to do? What does she know about cutting a mitred corner? She's here to pass the tools. I'm the brains of the outfit. She is just the mate. I say as much, just speaking my mind as I always do. She gets quite upset. She says, "Why shouldn't I tell you when you are wrong. I'm as much entitled to an opinion as you are and you ARE wrong."

We argue for quite a while, when suddenly in the middle of her explanation I realise she has been right about the mitre. I had been about to ruin a whole side of surround. I have to admit to her that she isn't just a pretty face. The arguments don't matter. We always end up with a cuddle. I guess we are in for a few arguments.

I don't bargain for the row we have in Woolworths. It is the last Saturday afternoon before Joan goes ahead of me to spend a week in Liverpool helping to make the final arrangements for the wedding. Somehow she has managed to find a dress. I haven't seen it but she says it is mid-calf in length with a full skirt (she knows I like full skirts) which later she can wear for dances. We know that Neil, as my best man, is giving us a canteen of cutlery as his wedding present. I am giving him a golf caddy. I suggest to Joan that we buy some cheap cutlery for everyday use. She picks up four each of soup spoons, dessert spoons, and medium-sized knives and forks.

I say, "You'll need dinner-sized knives and forks."

"Why?"

"Because for a joint it is the correct thing. I should know. I worked as a waiter for years before the war."

"And when will we be having a joint? It is still rationing and we only have two ration books. We'll be eating meals like sausage and chips or bacon and eggs, so we can get on fine with the smaller size of knives and forks. We will be eating breakfasts and high teas most of the time."

"We'll be entertaining, too."

"So then we'll use the ones from the canteen."

"In that case it is your choice. I thought you'd want to be correct."

Without warning she flings the whole lot back on the counter and stamps off. I lose her among the Saturday

16

shoppers for the next half hour. I think maybe she has pre-wedding nerves or could even be harbouring a few doubts about whether we should be getting married at all. I have no such doubts. I flatter myself that it will just take a bit of time for her to adjust. It would be foolish for me to think I could change. I've been a bachelor too long for that.

CHAPTER
TWO

Neil and I travel by train to Liverpool on the Friday before the wedding and Mrs Lowe, Joan's mother, arranges for us to stay with friends. It amuses me that Millie, our hostess, takes it for granted that Neil and I will not mind sharing a double bed. Neil is appalled.

Neither Joan nor I suffer from nerves at the service when the vicar, well-known to Joan but with whom we both spent an hour on Friday evening, greets us with "Enjoy the service". I'm quite staggered that although I am wearing a light grey lounge suit, Joan looks every inch a bride. I don't know how the Lowes manage it but the trestle tables and benches have been lent by the church and the crockery borrowed from Alfred Holt's hospitality ship, the *Galatea*, where Mr Lowe works. The food, roast turkey with large tins of ham and tins of real butter, some of it sent during the war years by friends whom Mr Lowe made in Australia, has not been seen by any of us since rationing began.

Somehow or other the thirty or so guests are squeezed in while Mrs Lowe's cronies are all helping serve from the kitchen or at table. Tom and Annie, Maisie and Kat, who is our little flower girl, Nan and Alex Anderson have arrived in Liverpool either the previous night or the Saturday morning and will be staying overnight with friends or neighbours of the Lowe family.

Tom and Bob give great speeches but Neil, surprisingly, is a bag of nerves. He can hardly hold the greetings telegrams. The speech of the father of the bride receives riotous applause from the Scottish contingent because he gives me a build-up and stresses how lucky his daughter is to be marrying me. He suddenly remembers to include a few observations about Joan, adding as a final warning, "Never put her in charge of the money," a remark greeted by gales of laughter and a resigned smile on the face of my mother-in-law. It is all over too quickly and half-way through the festivities, it seems to me, Joan and I are leaving and I am really sorry that we are not staying longer to enjoy ourselves with everybody else. I fancy Joan thinks it is more romantic to be going off on our own. We end up in a first class overnight sleeper and arrive back in Glasgow to spend Sunday in our new home. Joan looks a bit surprised when I suggest it would be a good idea to spend most of the day getting a skin on the lino. I explain it is to make life easier for her — get a skin on the lino and then it will only need a polish once a week.

I have the Monday off work so we go into town to take in a cinema and have a meal out. There's not been time for much of that between January and March. No phones have yet been installed on our housing estate and we have been placed in a queue to get a party line when they do start putting them in. We pass a phone box outside Central Station as we are about to board a local train to take us home. I suggest we give Neil a ring, adding it would be good to hear how the reception went off after we left. I say to Joan, "Is it okay with you if we ask Neil for tea one night this week? He'd get a kick out of being our first visitor." She agrees but we are both taken aback when he says he can come up the very next day for his tea. That first night, Joan grills the liver she has bought for our supper and it turns out like shoe leather. We ditch it and she is in tears.

I have to get back to the office on Tuesday but Joan has another couple of days off so I say I'll see her when I come home for lunch. Joan spends the morning shopping and cooking. Lunch makes up for the disaster of the previous night. We eat roast pork chops, ten roast potatoes and a whole cauliflower between us. Joan says we have no proper plates to eat from for tea and no electric kettle so I suggest she leave all the dishes on the table and accompany me into town to get the things she needs. It seems to me there will be plenty of time for her to get back home and prepare the tea with which she will want to impress our first visitor.

It is 5.30p.m. when I walk to the bus stop in Glassford Street. Imagine my astonishment when I see Joan in the queue. She is loaded with parcels but her face lights up as she sees me. I am not pleased: "What are you doing here? Why for heaven's sake are you not at home getting the tea ready? Don't you realise that Neil could be knocking on the door to find no one in?"

Joan tells me a long story about trying to choose a cookery book and putting down the plates and the kettle while she studied the merits of a shelf-full. It was only when she reached the bus queue an hour ago that she remembered she had left the kettle behind in the bookshop, so she had to trail all the way back to retrieve it. I'm not impressed by the tale nor the glimpse of the new kettle which she gives me. "Copper!" I say, "What possessed you to buy a copper kettle? Most electric kettles are chrome and don't require cleaning. You'll never be done cleaning this."

"Don't you think it is a beautiful colour?" she asks me.

When we get in the house I ask, "What are we having for tea?" Apparently it is to be ham and egg and chips. "Right," I say, "let's just hope that Neil hasn't been and gone away again. You get rid of the lunch dishes. I'll cook the tea."

We have our share of regular evening visitors. It is the first time in many years that, in a home of my own, I can return their unceasing hospitality. Joan buys tins of steak which are unrationed and creates meat pies. I explain to Joan how, in Glasgow, all the relatives and friends who have given us wedding presents have to be invited for a meal. We spread these out over several weeks.

When I get a free day I'm trying to dig over the waste ground two spades deep. The problem is that if the overturned ground is left for a week all the weeds have re-grown on it so I never seem to get beyond the patch at the bottom of the back garden. We have six-year old Kat to stay over a weekend. All through the war years and beyond she treated me like the Daddy whom she hardly ever saw when he was serving in the Royal Navy. Even though her dad is now at home, she finds it difficult to accept the fact that I have moved out. Joan tells her that she may think of our spare room as her room and she can come to stay as often as she likes. The first morning that she wakens up there and looks out at the back garden, she asks if she is allowed to play in the meadow.

The days are getting longer now so I'm working outside trying to build a coal bunker. The houses opposite are still being built so, as darkness falls, I meet most of my neighbours picking up a few bricks because it would seem we are all building our bunkers. I don't know whether to say hello or to pretend I haven't seen them.

Sundays follow a pattern. About half a dozen pals arrive at 10.00a.m. to give me a hand with the digging and laying of the concrete slabs for front and back paths. Joan clears up our breakfast and makes tea and toast for the workers. She seems to spend most of the morning peeling vegetables, making pastry and getting a dinner in the oven. She only knocks off when it is time for us all to pile in for elevenses. I must say she does us proud for Sunday lunch and I can see she has managed to get some cakes baked for the visitors we have invited for high tea. I suggest to her that maybe the chaps would enjoy one or two of these cakes with their post-lunch cup of tea and perhaps she could lay aside a few for the mid-afternoon cuppa. We return to the digging while she copes with the dirty dishes. She seems to be taking more cakes out of the oven and trying to get a tea-table set in the living room as, at about five o'clock we are packing up for the lads to get off home. I manage to grab a bath and a shave in time to greet the evening visitors. Doing this most Sundays is getting Joan into a good routine, even if it does often have to be a cold salad tea.

Every second week I am out on inspection with one of my travellers. We start on the Friday when they collect most of their customer cash. I am likely to be on the job until ten o'clock at night, climbing stairs and knocking doors. Saturday is more of the same but I knock off in the early afternoon. Monday, Tuesday and Wednesday I'm likely to finish mid-afternoon. My travellers know that I'm not one who wants to stop for teas and coffees or lunch, so we work right through. Every Thursday I see all my travellers in the office and it is after 7.30p.m. when I get home. Alternate weeks I am entirely in the office. These alternate weeks work in better with Joan's working day. She gets home about 4.30p.m. and has a meal ready for us both when I come in at six o'clock. She does not come home for lunch but I do because my lunch hour is too long to fill in if I stay in town.

When I come home mid-afternoon after working right through with a traveller, I am pretty hungry. As part of her wedding present to us, Maisie gave us a pressure cooker, the twin of one she uses daily. It means Joan can prepare the vegetables the night before and leave them together with the meat in the pressure cooker so that when I come in all I have to do is switch on the power. I've often just cleared away when Joan gets home from school. She is ready for her tea at about six o'clock but I am not. We are seldom eating before half past seven so it makes for quite a short evening which Joan frequently spends doing marking or lesson preparation.

One night recently I asked Joan what I was to take for my lunch the next day. She gave me a choice of about four things. Quite innocently I asked, "Is that it? Just one of those four items?" She gave me a rather hard look and a somewhat terse "That's it." I made no further comment. I know when to keep my mouth shut. As far as Joan knows, I am to this day ignorant of what went on after I went up to bed, leaving her downstairs. She must have spent the next hour taking every single can of food out of the kitchen cupboard and making a chain of items from the kitchen, through the hall and up the stairs to the bedroom door. How do I know? Because I got out of bed during that hour to use the upstairs toilet.

There was no sign of them next morning when I got up so I can only presume that she was cross with me for expecting more of a choice, but thought better of her actions and gathered all the tins back in the cupboard before she came to bed. Women are odd creatures!

CHAPTER
THREE

May 1953

I'm not the kind of man to go into detail about sexual matters so sufficient to say that, as a result of a conversation we had, Joan decided to register with one of the local doctors. I was more than shocked when, on her return, she told me the doctor thought she was most probably pregnant. I couldn't understand it because there was only one occasion when Joan had not taken contraceptive precautions. She said, "Aren't you pleased?"

How could I be pleased? We had very little time to go out and enjoy ourselves before we were married. I'd expected that for a year or two certainly we'd be making up for lost time. I tell her this. I say, "When will we know for certain?" She tells me that she asked the doctor if she couldn't have some kind of test and he just said, "Oh, it's a messy business and you are married, I suppose?" After Joan's indignant affirmation he'd added, "Well, it's the most predictable explanation of your condition and you can expect your baby in November."

November! I'm speechless. We only got married in March. What is everyone going to say? I am soon to find out. When Tom visits, he looks at Joan and asks, "And how is little November?" The next time he calls there's a twinkle in his eye as he changes this to, "And how is little September?" Everyone else just raises eyebrows and nods knowingly. I don't think I can live with this.

By the time we are watching the coronation of the young Queen Elizabeth on television, it has become apparent that the doctor was right. We are two of a number of friends sitting for hours in the home of Alex and Nan Anderson, joining in the day's celebrations. Joan is quite uncomfortable sitting for this length of time and is glad to get home.

The schools break up at the end of June. From school Joan rings up the Education Offices to tell them that our baby is to be born in November and to confirm that she will not be teaching after the term ends. The answer she receives is, "We allow you to teach until three months before the birth of the child so if you return for the one or two weeks following the holiday, you will be paid up to the end of November."

Joan persists: "But I don't intend to return to teaching. I won't be coming back after the baby is born or at any time in the foreseeable future."

"In Glasgow that is not a requirement. You will receive your last salary cheque once the baby is born."

Neither of us can believe it. Joan has only given service to Glasgow for less than two school terms and the pay will carry on until nearly Christmas.

Maybe things are working out for the best after all. Joan has not much enjoyed teaching in Glasgow. Her teaching here is a far cry from the involvement she had in her Liverpool school. Even though it was a primary department, a keen young staff put in many extra hours to carry out school projects concluding with dramatic productions in which all pupils played a part. Joan wrote the scripts and choreographed the free mime and movement while other members of staff taught the choir and folk dancers. They made their own scenery and costumes and Joan was overall responsible for the entire production with a cast of over a hundred children. She used to write about these things in her letters.

I wouldn't want her to get that involved in her work here. I was never too happy about having a wife who went out to work but Joan was keen to carry on teaching. She argued that when the only people she knew in Glasgow were my friends, she really needed to have interests of her own. We don't have to disagree about that any more. Joan will have the baby to look after and I think she is looking forward to that. It cannot be denied that this baby was not planned but I'm beginning to think it is quite a happy accident.

In July, at the Glasgow Fair, we spend my fortnight's holiday at Cullercoats, near Whitley Bay. We are late booking and we decide that, with future expenses looming, we will not indulge in anything too luxurious. We do not bargain for what we get. We are stuck in a small private hotel with a landlady who is a witch. She locks the door each night at 10.00p.m. and the first night we are locked out. I demand a key. Her meals are frugal and monotonous. Regularly the dessert course is some kind of blancmange. She is a Scot and, recognising Joan's northern English accent, she comments on the inability of the English to make good soup. To her surprise Joan freely admits this before adding, "But they can beat the Scots hollow at making puddings." This holiday was meant to be the honeymoon we were denied. It is an extremely poor substitute.

Joan's parents stay with us for a week in August, and Joan's mum helps her to shop for all the baby requirements such as the bedding for the cot and pram and turkish nappies by the dozen. I just fork out the cash. I tell Joan to bank her money that she still receives from Bath Street. It will be good for her to have a little nest egg of her own to spend how she pleases.

During the summer we have had some outings with Ralph and Margaret. Ralph is a huge American who was stationed here during the war when he met and married his school-teacher wife, Margaret. She and Joan have much in common. Ralph collects us in his firm's latest luxury car, sometimes a Jaguar, sometimes a Mercedes. He has had a variety of former occupations, jeweller, stage magician and many others. If all his wonderful stories can be believed, he has worked with Houdini and Tommy Cooper and he has even shot lions. His stories keep us well entertained as do the many tricks he can perform with his excellent sleight of hand. As a member of the Magic Circle he is often invited to perform at functions organised for charity by the police or the freemasons. He is one of a group of us who get together every few weeks for a boys' night out. We book a meal at one of the best hotels and a theatre show to follow. Because there are no drinkers among us, it is amusing to see the expression on the face of the wine waiter change when we order eight cokes or ginger beers.

Towards the end of the summer I realise that once we are parents we will be dependent on babysitters to let us out for an evening. Maybe even this autumn Joan is not always going to want to go out to the cinema. I suggest that we invest in some home entertainment and we install a television set with a nine-inch screen. On Saturday nights Margaret and Ralph come for cards and supper. We regularly take a break from playing the poker or canasta or pinochle in order to watch the *Black and White Minstrel Show* on the box. There is another popular TV show which we enjoy. It is called *I Married Joan*. The chief characters are a judge and his wife. The wife contrives to cause the most outrageous mishaps and he is always in despair trying to deal with the consequences. My Joan certainly gets herself into some difficult situations. It is just as well I keep my head.

God only knows how she manages it but one Saturday morning she succeeds in blowing the master electric fuse in the house. She says she was using the oven and all four of the cooking plates when one of the plates spluttered and sparked and went dead. After a while she switched it on again and the whole thing blew. The electrician we call in to repair it says it is the first time in his experience that anyone has managed to blow the main fuse in this way. Trust Joan to manage a first.

She has had a few cooking disasters since that first supper of uneatable liver. She gets on buses and trains going in the wrong direction or leaves things behind in shops. Regularly she mislays her engagement ring. It is just as well I have taken out insurance on it for the first year. Surely she can learn to take care of it in a year. I have told her that I am not renewing the insurance so she can keep up the payments if she so chooses. One day she takes it off while she is doing the washing. It is not until hours later when all the clothes have dried outside and been taken in that she realises she cannot remember where she laid it down. She is in a panic. I sit in the chair with the newspaper while she dashes up and down stairs and in and out of the garden hunting on the ground below the clothesline. She finds it in a bucket of starch under the sink. Apparently the last thing she washed was the apron she had been wearing. It had been dropped in the starch with the ring still inside the pocket. I find it difficult to understand why she cannot establish one place to put the ring whenever she takes it off. Unlike me she never seems to do anything routinely.

That is not to say that she isn't willing to tackle jobs some women might balk at. Now that we have a coal bunker I have shown her how to sort the coal with small bits to one side for starting the fire, large lumps in the middle to use once the fire has got under way and at the other end the slack for building it up to keep it going while we are out. When she has made a good job of it I praise her efforts, telling her it is great to see further proof of her superior education. When I am trying to put in some extra electric light sockets on the ground floor, she is willing to don my dungarees and crawl round on all fours under the floorboards to find the hole I have marked with the knitting needle from the floor above. This enables me to feed down the flex so she may feed it up to me in another marked spot.

I've shelved a couple of cupboards, but as soon as I have finished them she has them filled with her stuff. When I complain she says, "What are shelves for if not to put things on?" I suppose she has a point but I am forever making more shelves, hoping to get some space to put my own tools and gadgets.

Now that the garden paths are finished and I've managed to grass a lawn, we are free to attend church on a Sunday morning and we expect to become members of Cathcart South Church. Doctor Kerr, the minister, arranges to visit us. He says that Joan, having already been confirmed in the Church of England, is automatically accepted by the Church of Scotland. I, having formerly attended the Baptist church but not having undergone adult baptism, will need to attend a special service. It seems it will be a piece of cake compared with joining the Masons, which I did long ago simply because I was encouraged to do so by my uncle. Then it was a lot of mumbo jumbo, all a bit of a laugh, and although I attend some of the meetings I am no devotee. On the other hand they do a lot of good and they would never see any family of mine in need. This is worth some consideration when, with eleven years between Joan and me, the odds are it will be me that is first to kick the bucket.

I say to Joan, "Do you think we should offer the minister a sherry?"

"Why? We don't offer sherry to any of our other guests."

When he calls he is no hurry to leave and as he is good company I reconcile myself to the fact that I am not going to hear the football match which is tonight scheduled for radio. As Dr. Kerr leaves he looks at the clock: "Aren't we missing a match tonight? You should have mentioned it. I'll get home now so that we can both catch the second half." He does not get offered a sherry and some time later we discover that he preaches vehemently against the evils of drink.

As a result of joining the church, there is one evening when we are playing poker with Margaret and Ralph when there is a knock on the door. I leave the hands of cards on the table with a substantial kitty sitting in the middle. Our caller is a Mr Gillespie who is visiting to ask us if we will accept the envelopes for the church freewill offering scheme. I am thinking the card table will not provide a very good impression. I invite him into the hall saying, in a very audible voice, "It is nice to welcome somebody from THE CHURCH." I make some pretext to dally a moment before opening the door into the living room and introducing him to the company. I am relieved to see no tell-tale sign of the game that was in progress.

Joan trots off to bring in a supper tray while Ralph launches into some of his patter. He needs little persuasion to engage Mr Gillespie's attention in a very small ivory paddle which he produces from his pocket. Mr Gillespie is intrigued by the tiny fly which appears to be jumping from side to side of it. Our visitor stays for most of the evening, enjoying the supper and entertainment. Long after supper Margaret is still sitting with the table napkin in her lap. I lean across to remove it only to receive a quick, sharp slap on my wrist. Later I discover that below the napkin is the collection of coins that were in the kitty. Where did all the hands of cards vanish to? Certainly one of them reappears as our guest prepares to leave and Ralph, while pretending to help him on with his coat, withdraws from the inside pocket of the coat a five-card running flush.

Dr. Kerr greets us as we are leaving church the next morning. "Hang on," he says, "What's all this I hear about Big Ralph? Do you think we could persuade him to put on a show at our next social function?"

So the days go by, Neil, Margaret and Ralph, Tom and Annie, the Andersons and other couples becoming our regular visitors. We see Bob and Isabel less often as they become involved with bridge and bowling clubs.

Joan's choice of doctor turns out to be a fortunate one. It seems he has a particular interest and skill in dealing with mothers-to-be and babies. Some time ago he said that if Joan so wished she could give birth to the baby in our own home, where he would deliver it. He advised that, as it was a first baby, some relative or friend should be around to help through the first few days when Joan might be needing some support. We were glad when Joan's mother volunteered for the job.

Now, at the end of October, Mrs Lowe writes to say she is unable to fulfil the obligation because Mr Lowe is ill and she must remain at home to nurse him. We are in a predicament as it is too late to book Joan into a hospital. Our doctor suggests that if I can afford it he will make a reservation in Dawsholm, a private nursing home near Queen's Park. Seemingly he gives his services there as required. As he stresses the need for Joan to get some rest in the days after the birth, we are left with no alternative to his suggestion.

Saturday December 5th is a dark, wet day. Joan, daily keeping the washing down as her mother advises, is tired and fed up. The kitchen is draped with all the wet clothes and I've got the carpet up in the living room, trying to install wall lights on either side of the fireplace. This entails a fair amount of banging and the room is covered in dust from the disturbed plaster. Joan complains that there is nowhere to sit down so she escapes to lie on the bed upstairs and I get on with the job. The following day the world and his uncle call in to see why the baby has not yet put in an appearance. Joan copes manfully even though it is eleven o'clock when the last guest leaves. I tell Joan she must leave all the clearing up to me and go upstairs and get into bed. When I follow her upstairs some time later, she is still dressed. I ask why. Joan says, "I've just got up and redressed. I think you ought to take me to the nursing home."

Heavens above, why on earth could she not have made this decision when there was a houseful of people, any of whom could have gone to the phone on the main road some ten minutes away and ordered a taxi? I remember Mr Parrot, the neighbour who sold us our TV set and who kindly offered his help in an emergency. I race round the corner to his home and he drives me back to collect Joan and the case of baby stuff. It is well after midnight when I get back from the nursing home, relieved to pass all responsibility into better hands than mine.

I ring from work the next morning to be told that my daughter was born at 9.00a.m. What a clever child to have quashed all the rumours by arriving nine months to the day we were married.

The Dawsholm staff show me the baby as I am on the way to the ward to see Joan. I tell Joan. "She is quite the best-looking baby there. All the others are red and screwed up. She is just perfect."

We decide to register the baby's name as Jenny Linda. We choose Jenny because that seems to be the only name on which we can agree. As for the Linda, it is an affectionate reminder for us that throughout the pregnancy we referred to the forthcoming arrival as Belinda.

While Joan is away I manage to finish the wall lights and clean up the mess. I end up having to wash the carpet which we have had for less than a year. It shrinks. The pram and cot were ordered some time ago but there is no way I can arrange for them to be delivered when I am at work all day. Similarly I cannot take time off to collect mother and baby on the day they are due to come home, so the best I can do is to ask our next-door neighbour to pick them up by taxi. When I get home at teatime Jenny is asleep in a papier-mâché type baby bath. Apparently Joan asked the neighbour to pick this up from a local hardware shop so that she had somewhere to put the baby.

Quite soon everything falls into a routine. With some difficulty Joan is managing to feed the baby herself. While we wait for the milk supply to come in to meet Jenny's demand, Joan drinks gallons of water and I keep Jenny happy by giving her tiny spoonfuls of orange juice and bouncing her around to the pop songs of the 1950s — *Twenty tiny fingers, twenty tiny toes. . .* It works out well, especially the days I get home at lunch time for about an hour and a half. I can look after Jenny while Joan gets the lunch ready, and we can usually put Jenny for a sleep while we eat ours. The December days are too cold to put the pram outside or leave it in the unheated hall, so it sits in the living room. We have the oil heater to warm Jenny's room before she goes up there to sleep in her cot. We used to leave the heater on until one evening I went upstairs to find the room full of fumes.

Jenny only wakens once through the night for a feed. It is me who hears her crying and picks her up and brings her to Joan. I find it quite incredible that a mother can sleep through the crying of her own child. Joan says that in the nursing home there was a constant sound of babies crying in the night and it was easy to think of it as a flock of seagulls and shut it out. I can cuddle back to sleep while Joan is feeding and changing the baby and putting her back in her cot about an hour later. I need my night's rest. I've got a day's work to put in.

I don't know how Joan copes with washing nappies, baby clothes and cot sheets every day when she has to dry them indoors. Jenny is bathed in front of the fire every morning but I tell Joan that she must leave the bath for me to empty. It is far too heavy for her to lift. The pregnancy seems to have left Joan with a sore back. I spot a nursing chair in the warehouse and get it delivered.

Parcels arrive from Liverpool for our first Christmas in our own home. As well as presents there are home-made mince pies, Christmas cake and Christmas pudding. We buy a chicken for our Christmas dinner. When Christmas Day arrives, it is cold and sunny. It is the first chance I have had to push my new daughter in her new pram and it is a great feeling. We walk all the way to Govanhill to let Maisie and her family see the new baby. Maisie has invited neighbours in for Christmas dinner. The smell of roast sirloin of beef and roast potatoes fills the house. I refuse Maisie's invitation to stay for the meal, saying she has enough company already. Joan overrules me and tells Maisie she is starving and there is nothing we would like better than to join them. It is great that Joan is feeding the baby herself. It leaves us free to take her with us wherever we go, unencumbered by bottles.

Less than a week later we are preparing to celebrate the New Year. I explain to Joan how it is essential that for any visitors arriving, the house must be spotless and there must be plenty of food. I finish in the early afternoon of New Year's Eve and ask Joan how she has got on with the preparations. "I've spent the whole morning baking," she admits, "I haven't got round to any of the cleaning." I get busy polishing and hoovering and we are all set for the crowd of friends and neighbours who stay well into the morning of New Year's Day.

Next morning Joan says, "I had a dream last night, and Ralph was saying that he and Margaret were going to Liverpool to the races, so if we wanted we could go with them and they could drop us off to visit my family." I say, "Well you did have one or two drinks and you are not used to drinking like that. No wonder you were dreaming." It is not until later that I tell her it was no dream and we are to be ready for Ralph and Margaret to pick us up in the early evening.

It is a very frosty evening, and as we climb Shap there is a long line of stranded lorries and cars. We have no problem in Ralph's powerful car and we are all in high spirits. When we stop for petrol the attendant looks into the car and peers at Jenny who is fast asleep. Ralph accepts all the admiration, pretending it is his own child. "This child has travelled all over the world," he boasts and because he is a big American with the appropriate accent I daresay he is believed. As promised we spend the next day with Joan's family and Jenny is not a whit worse for the excursion.

Joan's brother and sister both manage to come up for the christening in February and we have a big party for them and all our friends. When our anniversary arrives on March 7th, I say to Joan, "Well, Sunshine, that is the first year of our married life over." Joan says, "Thank goodness for that." In response to my searching look she adds, "You must admit that in some ways the first year is a bit difficult. I mean there's a lot of adjusting to one another." I say firmly, "I am not conscious of any adjusting that had to be done." She smiles. "I know, Alex. That is because I was doing most of the adjusting."

I'm left puzzled but heartened when my next door neighbour tells me that Mr Sinclair, probably the most senior resident on this estate, has been heard to comment that if there was a prize for progress it would certainly go to Alexander Park. In one year he got married, furnished his house, dug his garden, laid his paths, put up his garden hut, built a coal bunker and found time to father an infant.

CHAPTER
FOUR

It seems to me that in no time at all Jenny is propped up in a highchair and being weaned on to mashed potato and stewed apple. Soon she is managing to feed herself, leaving us in no doubt that she dislikes porridge and spinach. The spoon goes down on the plate with such force that we now have porridge stains on the ceiling.

Joan's dad is not recovering from his illness and it would seem that there is little chance of her parents getting to Glasgow to see us, so we decide that Joan should go and visit them in Liverpool. Tom, who works as a chef on the railway, arranges dining room accommodation for Joan and Jenny. I cope on my own but I miss them, especially when their stay is extended due to a railway strike. The day they are travelling home Joan gets no further than Wigan. She is stranded in a waiting room there for eight hours. I go to Glasgow Central to meet them and I hang about for most of the evening. It is after ten o'clock when the train comes in. Joan says that she is worn out because Jenny never shut an eye all day. She feels more than a bit resentful when Jenny falls asleep within minutes of the taxi moving. I have Teddy sitting in the hall and seeing him as we open the door causes Jenny so much excitement that she is still wide-eyed and ready to play when we are dying to get to our beds.

While Joan was away I cooked one or two of my own meals. Knowing I was on my own our various friends invited me to eat with them. I had a bit of spare time so I reorganised all the kitchen cupboards. I also do a good job using wire wool to get all the black stuff off the inside of the pans. On Joan's return I am telling her about my efforts.

"It's so much easier to work properly if the items you most often use are at hand on the nearest shelf. Think of the time you can save not having to cross the kitchen for something you require every time you cook."

"I take it you'll be working in the kitchen from now on."

"Of course not. It's your kitchen. I just did it all to help you develop a bit of a routine."

"Well, I know it was all meant for my benefit but if I'm the one who is going to be working in the kitchen I hope you won't mind if I change things back to the way they were before I went away."

"You must do as you wish. It seems to me that you don't have any regular method of doing any job. I couldn't work that way."

"That's because you are you and I am me. I'm not trying to change you. Why should you insist on changing me? If you succeed you might end up regretting it. I certainly wouldn't be the person that you chose to marry. And, by the way, that black stuff you removed from the pans was the non-stick surface."

The next time Joan sees her parents is when we take our July holiday in Southport. We book in at a small hotel which caters for children. The Lowes urge us to leave Jenny with them until the Sunday so we can have a day to ourselves in Southport. They mean well and we think how much we would welcome just being on our own. We do not foresee that by the time Sunday arrives we are absolutely desperate to have our demanding little monster back with us.

It rains every day of the holiday. It is so windy that we can seldom risk walking along the sea front so our outings are confined to the local park and our activities to feeding the ducks. Jenny gets pushed everywhere in a pushchair. She grows accustomed to this VIP treatment and when we go back home she is not at all happy to sit in her pram outside with no attention.

Within a short time after this holiday Jenny is crawling on knees and forearms, leaving her hands free to grab everything within sight. She makes a beeline for the television.

I spend an entire afternoon telling her not to touch the knobs, but as soon as I raise my newspaper and she thinks I am not watching her she is back at the knobs. To reinforce my words I give her a little tap on the wrist every time she disobeys me and at the end of the afternoon I congratulate myself that my patience has paid off. I take some time explaining this procedure to Joan who says, "Well, that may work if you've got nothing to do except sit in the chair and watch her. It doesn't work when you have to get through all the chores or answer the doorbell or bring the washing in.

You should have a go at trying to stop her eating the soap when you are washing the kitchen floor."

Because Jenny is ready for bed between six and seven o'clock, it is seldom that we go out in the evening so the world and his uncle come to see us either after 7.00p.m. on weekdays or for a meal at weekends. A number of people gave us baby presents and the least we can do is have them for tea or supper, and I enjoy having company. I am always happy to give Joan a hand with preparation or clearing up.

I am quite unprepared for Joan exploding when I walk in one Saturday teatime. We've invited Archie and Gwen and Gwen's sister for tea. It was through meeting Archie on holiday that I switched from selling insurance to becoming a traveller for Simpson and Shaw. I am eternally grateful to him for that. Because I want everything to be just so, I note that before giving Jenny her tea in the highchair Joan has managed to set the table and prepare the meal. I go upstairs to have a wash and shave and come down having changed. I check up to see that Joan has put all the requirements on the table. I nip into the kitchen and bring back a dishtowel to remove finger marks from the outside of a glass sugar bowl. Joan is giving me one of her long looks. I smile and say, "Just giving your sugar bowl an extra polish, dear. A pity to spoil the table when everything else is just right."

"What a good thing you had time to check the sugar bowl," Joan says, and with her voice rising a full octave. "Now look at me. You are all fresh and dressed and I haven't had time to wash my face since seven o'clock this morning."

I just don't understand what causes her to fly off the handle when it is so obvious that I'm only concerned that my friends hold her in as high esteem as I do. Joan's behaviour seldom tallies with what I expected a wife to be like, and then again there are occasions like today when I am surprised that she so completely expresses a truly feminine characteristic. She wanted to look dressed up when I thought she looked fine as she was. She thought she looked scruffy and was angry because I hadn't noticed. Women!

Margaret and Ralph sometimes insist on returning our hospitality. They say we have to go to their house for a meal, put Jenny down at her usual bedtime in their bed and, without waking her up, Ralph will run us home at the end of the evening. I insist that we get ourselves over to their bungalow in Drumchapel by public transport. Carrying everything but the kitchen sink for Jenny's bedtime needs, we set off only to realise when we arrive that we have forgotten the one essential item, Jenny's special cot sheet. As a baby, Jenny was never given a dummy or anything from a bottle with a teat so she quite soon developed the habit of sucking the corner of her cot sheet. She refuses to settle without the sheet and the night we are at Margaret and Ralph's is no exception. There is nothing for it but to accept Ralph's offer to run us home after the meal is over.

In the July of 1955 we spend our summer holiday back in Morecambe. This is a favourite rendezvous for Glasgow people at the Fair. We meet up each day with

44

office friends of mine, Alex and Nan and Jack Pennington and his wife Rene. We have a good holiday.

Summer 1956

Jenny is still chewing the cot sheet even though she is two and a half years old. More than once Joan has cut the chewy patch from the previous sheet in order to patch it on to a new sheet.

A couple of months ago we decided that we did not want Jenny to be an only child so we are not surprised when we discover we are to have an addition to the family about the end of February. You could say we planned this baby in that we stopped using a contraceptive. Considering the fact that, soon after we were married, I told Joan that I thought sex was an over-rated pastime, it seems that in our case it is highly successful in producing offspring. We are a couple of amateurs where sex is concerned. Neither of us had any pre-marital experience in this department and practice has not produced a whole lot of progress. I was a bit shocked when Joan suggested that I study an instruction book she had bought. She was very understanding when I said I'd rather not and that I would prefer the whole thing to stay spontaneous and natural.

Joan's dad died at the beginning of last year so we have had her mother staying with us a couple of times and some week-long visits from friends in Liverpool who were at the wedding. There are times when I think we should call our home the Braehead Hotel but for

Joan's sake it is a good thing that her friends are willing to come up by train or car. Her sister, Thelma, has arranged to take time off so that Joan can have this baby at home.

Chiefly through her attendance at the baby clinic, Joan has made several friends and so from time to time one will volunteer as a babysitter to let us out to the local cinema. Joan's particular friend is Sheena whose baby, Lorna, was born in Dawsholm while Joan was there. Sheena lives at the bottom of the hill so she brings Lorna with her when she comes for a morning coffee. When, at the crawling stage, the children were put in the playpen, Joan and Sheena got no peace, so they have solved this by giving the children the whole of the floor space while they sit inside the playpen to drink their coffee.

Joan is bigger with this baby and because she is normally like a rake she feels awkward. She is forever dropping things and having to kneel down to mop up the spills and the breakages. Cooking smells make her nauseous and the later in the day this is the worse she feels. I still have to do my Friday evenings out with a traveller, checking his books. We have a phone now so I can ring Joan to let her know when I am on my way home so she can start to cook my supper. This has disastrous results one evening when I phone, only to be later held up. I am coming through the kitchen door when Joan, on her knees barks, "You can't come in this way. Go round to the front door and I'll let you in." I do as directed and, sensing a bit of a crisis, I sit in the front room waiting for my supper. A while goes by and then I hear a clatter from the kitchen and soon afterwards Joan dumps down a plate of ham and egg and chips. I have the temerity to ask, "Has that egg come off the floor?" Joan is very terse. "It has. So what?"

"Fine," I say and pick up my knife and fork. I'm learning when it is safer to keep my thoughts to myself.

I later find out that Joan had cooked and disposed of two suppers while waiting for me to appear. She had spilt the hot dripping from the chip pan and was trying to mop it up when I had tried to enter. With the third supper in her hand she had skidded on the newly washed floor, the plate of food had upset and, determined not to cook a fourth supper, she had scraped it all back on to the plate.

CHAPTER
FIVE

March 1957

I am over the moon. We have a son. We hadn't even considered a name for a boy. I was so sure it would be another girl and happy that it should be so. I didn't guess how great it would be to have one of each. When I announce the good news at work someone says, "That's it then, Alex. You have a gentleman's family." I don't think I've ever heard that expression before. I just know I feel like a lord.

Scott is a fortnight late in arriving so he has feet like a frogman. Thelma is coping very well with meals and with looking after Jenny. Scott sleeps a lot and it would appear that Jenny is quite happy to have her own baby brother. Joan involves her in fetching items from the baby basket and lets her apply the talcum powder, but Jenny is very demanding. One minute she wants to play outside with her friend, Marie, the next she is wanting to come back into the house. She cannot reach door handles so while trying to feed Scott Joan is bobbing up and down to attend to Jenny. It is all a bit wearing for her.

Jenny persists in getting her own way and is most unwilling to do as she is told. Joan reasons with her all the time. I say, "This is ridiculous, you can't reason with a three-year old." When I tell Jenny to do something or, more often than not, to stop behaving badly, and she comes up with her usual, "Why?" I say, "Because I am your Daddy and I say so." Now and again I give her a little tap to reinforce this. It seems to work well.

One day I come home and Joan is upset. "I don't know what I am going to do. Mrs Green says she caught Jenny trying to climb into the pram with her one-year old and Mrs Clark complains that Jenny was throwing stones at her little boy. Someone in the next avenue rang up to say Jenny had pushed her little girl off her tricycle and was hitting other children." I tell Joan that she will just have to keep Jenny indoors. Joan complains that she would be the one to suffer most from that solution. She adds that my smacking could be giving the wrong pattern to imitate and maybe we should try out a spell of setting a different example. Joan writes regularly to her mother, who has no telephone. In one of her replies her mum suggests that, as Joan herself has quite a will and married someone equally endowed, it is hardly surprising that our daughter has inherited a double dose.

Scott is only months old when he has to go into hospital with a suspected hernia. He is kept in overnight but as it turns out there does not have to be surgery because it is corrected by manipulation and we are allowed to collect him the following day.

It is this summer that Joyce, a friend of Joan's from Australia, comes to visit us. It is a prolonged stay because she develops jaundice soon after she arrives but not before she has, at her own request, taken Jenny out for the day. They sail down the Clyde. Each time someone on board refers to the seagulls Jenny corrects them by saying they are pigeons. Joyce is worn out trying to cope with such a stubborn child. This is the last outing Joyce takes for several weeks. She is confined to bed and Joan runs up and down with her meals. One morning, while Joan is out shopping, the doctor calls and pronounces Joyce fit to get out of bed. When Joan comes home, it is to find a note from Joyce to say she has gone to Loch Lomond for the day. I am really angry. I think the least she could have done in return for all the recent attention she has received was to give a hand with the chores for a day. I say, "If she's fit to go out for the day, she's fit to leave. Blame it on me if you like but tell her we've had enough of her."

The year that we were expecting Scott, we had gone on holiday to Whitley Bay with Jack Pennington and his wife and we plan to go on holiday with them again this year. Jack is a work colleague of mine and his wife is of West Indian parentage. They have no children but they love children and often visit us. Jack insists on volunteering to do the babysitting to enable us to have an anniversary outing. He comes to tea, and the children are all fed and washed and ready for bed before we leave. Jenny likes to have the Ladybird rhyming stories read to her before she goes to bed so Jack is quite prepared to read from *Five Little Kittens* while we get ourselves ready. Jenny tells him if he misses a page and often joins in the rhyme. "This child can read," Jack says in amazement, but we assure him it only seems like that because she can recite so much of the story by heart. He is not convinced.

We have acquired a second-hand tape recorder. Brendan Green in the house opposite is an auctioneer and is willing to put in a bid on our behalf. Brendan and Mary Green are never short of babysitters whom they are willing to share with us. Marie, their little girl, has started school at the convent just around the corner. The nuns encourage their pupils to bring their friends on Saturday mornings. Jenny is a regular visitor. She sometimes sits in the little basket chair I brought home for her. She drapes a cloth over her head and says she is Sister Mary Joseph. She tells us that she will soon be going to Marie's convent school. Joan tells her that she will be going to Limewood School. She tries to explain that Marie goes to the convent school because her family go to a different church from us. Jenny persists that the nuns say she can go to their school. Joan says, "Well, we are your mummy and daddy and we say you will be going to Limewood." Jenny caps this with, "But, Mummy, the nuns are the spirit of God." It seems that the nuns use their Saturday mornings very profitably.

Joan says her supply of stories is running out. Whether Joan is cleaning the fireplace, peeling potatoes or even taking the children into town on the train, Jenny insists there be a story to accompany the procedure. Joan says she has told Jenny every fairy story, every story she has ever come across in school reading books and every bible story that could be told to a child. At present she is even telling her the story of the two little girls in *Green Dolphin Country* that she is reading herself.

Joan tries to get Jenny absorbed in other kinds of activity. For a long time Jenny has enjoyed the cut-out cardboard doll figures which come in books complete with the doll's wardrobe. Joan buys old pattern books from dress material departments in the town stores and teaches Jenny to cut out the figures. Both children are settled in bed around seven o'clock except for the Saturday nights when Margaret and Ralph arrive just as they have been put upstairs. Ralph goes up to say goodnight to them. This is his excuse for the ensuing pillow fight with all the wild shrieks which accompany it.

Jenny is content to go to bed at the same time as Scott just so long as she is allowed an extra half hour to play in bed. Her play consists of looking at picture books or doing her cut-outs. I question the wisdom of letting a four-year old loose with scissors when she could possibly find distraction in cutting into the wallpaper or bedclothes but this never happens.

June 1958

Towards the end of the school term Joan visits our local Limewood School to enrol Jenny for the new term beginning in August. She is told Jenny's December birthday renders this impossible. Jenny will not start school until February 1959. Straight from this encounter Joan gets on a bus into town and comes back with the six introductory reading books of the *Janet and John* series. Jenny knows the sounds of all the letters because we regularly play a game with a small-case plastic alphabet. Within a week she is through Book One and in a month she has mastered all six books. Marie passes her convent school reading books on to Jenny, and Joan helps her to choose easy books from the library.

For Jenny's fifth birthday the neighbouring children are invited to our house for a party. Joan and I have the food and games planned in advance. Margaret and Ralph come to join in. About halfway through the afternoon Ralph takes over. He has brought a huge suitcase full of tricks and favours. He keeps these infants entranced for over an hour, producing rabbits out of hats, bunches of flowers out of empty vases and all manner of other things out of nowhere. Finally he flings open the lid of the suitcase and in all directions throws out a never-ending abundance of streamers, whistles, balloons and hooters. The four of us sit drinking tea in the kitchen while the unsupervised guests have a wonderful time before they go home with their loot.

For the following week any contact with the parents of the children brings forth protests of, "How on earth are we supposed to follow that when it is our turn to give a party? And the presents they brought home, all produced by a real, live magician! There's no way we can compete on that scale." Actually, Ralph has only to put a fez on his head to look like Tommy Cooper's double.

Joan and I take it in turns to put in an appearance at the Sunday morning church service. If arrangements have been made for an afternoon visit to friends or relatives, it is a bit of a rush to get the lunch over before we set out on public transport. As we are about to leave the house on one of these occasions, I look at Scott, his usual placid self, standing there kitted out in his Sunday best.

I say to Joan, "He looks a bit odd."

"What do you mean, a bit odd?"

"It's that coat. It doesn't seem to fit him properly."

"Of course it fits him. You deal with it. I can't do everything myself."

I remove Scott's coat and find the coat-hanger still inside it. Perhaps Scott has already learned to accept the shortcomings of his mother.

It is around this time that my back, often a source of pain, begins to give me real trouble. On the doctor's recommendation I have packed in the golf, which I seldom had time to play anyway. Finally I am confined to bed. It is summer, so for most of the day the children play outside. Joan brings up my teatime meal and she is in the kitchen with Jenny and Scott together in the bath. Jenny is singing one of her daily calypsos: "Today I was playing with Marie and Peter. Peter did his wee-wee standing up behind the garage. Marie says we have not to tell." Mr Symons, one of the owners of Simpson and Shaw, pops in to see me. He tells me not to worry about cash. He assures me I will be paid indefinitely. Later, Mr Lewis, my boss, phones, one of his daily interrogations demanding to know how soon I can promise to be back on the job.

Joan appears upstairs again with the children, bringing them in to see me to say goodnight. They are both bouncing around on the bed. Jenny says her nightly prayer: "God bless Mummy, God bless Daddy. God bless Scott. God bless me and make me a good girl. Amen." As she reaches the end she says, "Now Scott has to say his prayers." Because he follows Jenny's bidding at all times, Scott puts his hands together, closes his eyes and stumbles through "God bless Mummy. God bless Daddy. God bless me and make me a good girl."

"He didn't say God bless Jenny and how can God make him a good girl when he's a boy?" On Jenny's insistence Scott has a second attempt but repeats the "Make me a good girl."

Even later that evening a couple of my office colleagues call in to see if I am faking it. Joan is grateful to the tallest one who is willing to tackle a huge moth and a couple of daddy-long-legs. Joan cannot suffer either of these creatures in the house.

This is the year when Joan's friend, Sheena, gives birth to her second baby, a little boy who is called Ross. About a month after the birth she and Bob, her husband, are driving to Edinburgh to visit Sheena's parents. They are involved in a road accident in which her husband and children survive but Sheena, in the front passenger seat is killed outright. Sheena is in her early twenties and it is very sad as Bob tries to cope. His young sister of eighteen comes to live with them.

Ross becomes her baby and we feel for Lorna in that her Aunt Evelyn finds it difficult to find enough time in her day to cope with a motherless four-year old. From then on we try to include Lorna in our family outings and treats. A Saturday morning trip into town is one of these regular outings.

For Jenny's third Christmas we had bought her a toy piano. At the time there was a Saturday morning radio programme called *Children's Favourites* in which listeners' request records were played. We regularly heard *Nellie the Elephant, Tubby the Tuba, Sparky's Magic Piano*, items from the *Nutcracker Suite* and the *Dance of the Trolls* from *Peer Gynt*. It was the last of these tunes which Jenny could imitate on her toy piano. I'm pretty sure that it was an accident the first time she found she had produced the same notes, but that she could replay it at will led us to think that this musical talent should be encouraged. Thus it is that Joan takes both Jenny and Lorna to a morning class in a form of eurhythmics, mostly for under-fives. The idea underlying the class is that if the children become skilled in using left and right sides of their bodies independently, they will be the better suited for learning to play a musical instrument.

The children enjoy what is for them a dancing lesson. For the hour that the lesson is in progress some of the mothers enjoy a coffee and cake in Fuller's café. Scott is one of the café participants. He enjoys the train outings and the chocolate cake. Scott is more easily pleased than ever Jenny was or is. When I read him a bedtime story he always asks for *The Three Bears*, and when asked to recite a nursery rhyme it is always *Little Jack Horner*. I nearly always come home on a Saturday with a little present for each of the children. For Jenny it is often a story book and for Scott it is a little Matchbox or Corgi car. He plays for hours with two little cars on the nearest windowsill.

Jimmy Wilson, another office colleague of mine, is house-hunting. He and his wife and two little boys call in one Sunday afternoon to get an idea of how the Simshill house which they are considering, and which is similar to ours, would look when furnished. After they have left Jenny says, "Gerald was a very naughty boy. He did his wee-wee standing up. When I told you that Peter did that in the garden, you said it was naughty."

"Only because he went behind the garage instead of in the bathroom," says Joan, launching into a long explanation about how little boys are made differently from little girls and pointing out that Jenny has bathed with Scott and seen his extra appendage.

"Oh, that!" says Jenny dismissively, "I had one of those when I was little."

Joan worries about how Jenny will fare at the hands of her first teacher. "Children who try to put their teacher right do not score too highly in the favour stakes. Jenny is likely to start off on the wrong foot and I don't envy her teacher's job."

Joan has worried unnecessarily. The first class is taught by Miss Robertson, the head of the infant school, who has a no-nonsense approach exactly suited to Jenny's needs.

We ask Jenny to tell us about her first day.

"We have a very naughty boy in our class."

"Oh, what did he do that was so naughty?"

"When he was drinking his milk, he broke his straw."

Three cheers for Miss Robertson. She has, on day one, succeeded in making Jenny appreciate the omnipotence of the teacher. Jenny has met her match.

At some point during that first term Joan is asked if she will go into Limewood School to take a class while one of the teachers is away sick. She explains that this is not possible because she has a two-year old and she has no one to look after him in her absence. Immediately she is told, "Just bring him with you". On the first afternoon Scott falls asleep on the classroom floor and, ridden with guilt, Joan tells the headmaster that she feels she cannot continue. He begs her to stay to finish the week, chiefly because Bath Street are unable to get their sums right if they have to calculate pay for a part-week. Joan does stay for the other four days and about a month later receives a cheque for twenty pounds. I tell Joan to put it in her bank, something to have to call her own.

I pay all the big bills and give Joan seven pounds a week housekeeping money. She buys the food, coal, cleaning materials, toilet requisites and the smaller items of clothing needed for herself and the children. I am somewhat shocked when I see the cheap tawdry bag she is sending to her mother as a Mother's Day present. I say, "Surely you can do better than that. It's not the kind of present I'd give my mother if she were still alive." When Joan tells me that her housekeeping money will not stretch to meet the cost of presents, I decide that instead of giving Joan extra housekeeping I will instead put a weekly sum of money into a joint kitty so there is a fund to meet such contingencies.

During her first year at school Jenny brings home measles and chicken-pox. Measles are passed on to Scott but he seems to be escaping chicken pox until the day before we are about to go to Southport on holiday. We have already contacted the people who own the hotel where we stay. They cater specially for children, even providing a babysitting service, and we feel we owe it to them to say we may be transmitting chicken-pox. They say that their children have already had it and as for children of guests, we will be doing them a favour in that their offspring will not be affected during the holiday and, should it develop on their return home, then it won't be likely to strike later and prevent some future holiday. Our doctor agrees.

CHAPTER
SIX

Spring 1961

I am glad to say we are past the stage when Jenny insisted on reading the contents of the sauce bottle at every meal. Now she just talks all the time, and when we make time for Scott to get a word in, he is in tears because by then he has forgotten what he was going to say. She has moved up to Mrs Smith's class. Every second sentence begins with, "Mrs Smith says. . ." Mrs Smith is to our home what Confucius is to the homes of China.

Another teacher from Limewood school comes to see if Joan will consider assisting for one term while they are a teacher short on the staff. Joan says, "Apparently Glasgow is so short of teachers that as the child of a teacher Scott would immediately be given a free place in a day nursery. I can't contemplate it. You know what he's like. He cries if I even go out of the room."

"All the better reason for giving him a shot of nursery school," I argue. "He's too much of a Mummy's boy, and the money would come in handy. Remember you earned twenty pounds in that week you did a couple of years ago. Also, you say you want to go back to teaching once the kids are both in school. What

60

could be better than a school on the doorstep. This is an opportunity to get where you want through the back door."

So Joan goes back to teaching. I console myself that I still earn the bread and butter but she puts the jam on it. Actually at the end of the first term she receives a letter thanking her for a term's service and, while she thinks that is the end of it, I am not at all surprised when she is taken on for the next term and the next term and the next and so on because there is still a teacher shortage. I make it clear to Joan that I do not want to come home to waiting for meals to be cooked or being asked to do the hoovering so it might be an idea to use some of her money to pay for help in the house. The various attempts that Joan makes to do this turn out very unsatisfactory so she is forced to cope without help.

It is just around this time that I take back trouble again and I end up in traction in hospital for a week. It is absolute torture, not unlike the medieval rack, I imagine. The nurses are kind and one of them offers to give me a shave. As she finishes I say, "You are very professional, I never once felt that razor." I then discover that she had not put any blade in the razor.

Joan takes Scott to the nursery each morning by bus, spends the day at school, collects him after four and drops in to see me before going home to make the tea. Most nights she gets a babysitter so that she can visit me. Once or twice Neil volunteers to bring her by car. Joan says that on their return home he tends to stay for the rest of the evening and she is doing schoolwork and housework after he has left.

As I entered hospital we had a new sink unit being installed. Joan says that, now the workmen have left, the kitchen is a mess and she has no time to clear it up. She prevails upon one of the nursery cleaners to do just this, putting the key in her hand and telling her how to find her way to the house. Meantime she approaches a Mrs McMaster who cleans for a neighbour to include our house for two mornings each week. Mrs McMaster comes to us for the next fourteen years.

Summer 1962

Scott starts school so now both children are attending Limewood, where Joan is regularly re-engaged for each school year. I decide we can afford to buy a new car. I am quite apprehensive driving it home through the town when I have not driven for nearly nine years. In the Anglia we can now take trips to the seaside and we go picking blackberries with two friends, Dave and Enid. We use holiday weekends to go to see Joan's family in Liverpool. We drive down the A74 and it is very exciting to travel on the first stretches of the M6 which are being constructed south of Carlisle. On one of these trips we stop at the services which the children, because of its peculiar shape, have christened the mushroom. Using the coffee dispenser for the first time, I am holding the cup under one of the taps while from another the coffee is pouring down a sink.

We still have to negotiate Shap on the old road where, on our return journey, the Anglia can be stuck behind a slow lorry all the way to Penrith. On holiday weekends there are anything up to two-hour hold-ups at Penrith and Kendal. We travel with enough food to withstand a siege; chicken drumsticks and sausages as well as sandwiches. We operate hand signals through a rolled down window. There are no seat belts and no restrictions to children sitting in the front passenger seat. My passengers take turns to have this privilege. I buy Scott a miniature steering wheel which sticks on to the dashboard and he can sit for hours, perfectly happy.

Now that we have a car we can drive to Morecambe for our summer holiday. An afternoon at the pleasure beach proves both costly and unrewarding. It seems that paying for their ride on one contraption only leads to a demand for another ride on something else. It results in quarrels and tears and the children would appear to be forever dissatisfied. We agree that we will spend the other days on the beach or the crazy golf.

On our last morning it is raining. I say, "Your mum and I have to do some shopping for holiday presents. Make up your minds on where you want to go and we'll drop you there to spend as long as you wish. You can tell us when to pick you up and take you to the next choice." The first selected venue is the waxworks. In the car, on our way to the next venue, Jenny asks, "What is Christine Keeler famous for?"

Joan says, "The correct word would be 'infamous'. She was a prostitute."

"What's a prostitute?"

"Someone who takes money from men by pretending to be in love with them."

We think that is the end of the matter but when, on our return to Glasgow, Joan collects Jenny from Sunday School the teacher confronts her. "When we asked for pupils to come forward to talk about high spots in their summer holiday, Jenny launched into a tale about Christine Keeler. She was quite prepared to explain what a prostitute was but we managed to get her back in her seat. Hardly a subject for Sunday School, you'll agree."

Dave and Enid suggest we employ a young friend of theirs to build us a garage, with their own fourteen-year old son giving him a hand. This gives rise to some problems. Our young man is a meticulous workman but fails to warn me in advance when the building materials are due to arrive. One Saturday morning a lorry, carrying ready-mixed cement arrives at the door. The driver demands payment on delivery. Joan rings me to explain that he will only deliver if he gets the money. I say, "Okay. Tell him if he insists, he will just have to take it away."

Of course he cannot do this, the cement will be useless. As I foresee, he delivers it, but not before calling his boss from his lorry in a voice which echoes the length of the avenue, "There's a woman here who hasn't got the money to pay." Joan is embarrassed but laughs about it afterwards, while I tell my builder that in future when he arranges for a delivery he must give me some prior notice.

On Tuesday afternoons I collect the family from school and we drive to a Shawlands cinema. There we can go into a restaurant to enjoy a high tea and still get into the cinema at a reduced rate before five o'clock. The ham and eggs or fish and chips cost two shillings and sixpence so Joan forks out the ten shillings for the meal and I provide the ten shillings for the seats in the cinema. For the children's sake we endure Norman Wisdom comedies but I soon wean them on to submarine films. I've made certain that no one develops a taste for westerns.

Jenny has taken up the fiddle at school. In the early stages it is pretty deadly. I instruct Joan, "Encourage her to get her practice over before I get home." This is to lead to a bit of misunderstanding on the part of the music teacher. It is the last week of October, a week in which Jenny has her regular night at the Brownies, another taken up with Hallowe'en activity, and yet another when we are coming home at about eight o'clock after tea and cinema.

Joan says, "No hanging about. You've got half an hour to get yourselves to bed."

"What about my violin practice?"

"That will have to wait for another night."

"But that's what you said last night and the night before and it's my lesson tomorrow. What will I tell Mr Rennie?"

"You'll just have to explain that it's been a busy week."

Mr Rennie approaches Joan in school the next day, "What kind of a monster are you married to? Jenny tells me she is not allowed to play the violin if her father is in the house."

We are doing a spot of decorating in our hall. Joan takes herself to Sanderson's to choose wallpaper. When she has finally decided on the pattern, she cannot remember how many rolls will be required. The sales assistant suggests that she ring home to check this. With the phone in her hand she cannot remember her home number and has to ask for a telephone directory. Joan has absolutely no memory for numbers. To save her life she couldn't tell you the number of the car and she says someone only has to ask for a number to put her in a panic.

I tell Joan that when she is shopping in town she should not encumber herself with loads of parcels. "You know where I leave the car outside the office and you have a car key. Just put the bags in the boot for me to bring home." I happen to come out of the office one day to see her struggling to fit the key into the boot of a car which is not mine. "For heaven's sake what are you doing? That's not our car."

"Well, I thought it was. It's the same colour as ours."

One very wet day I pick her up from school to do some local shopping. I say, "I'll park outside the shop but I'm not really allowed to park here at this time of day. I might have to move on." Some time later she emerges from the shop, weighed down by the groceries. She struggles with the passenger door, settles herself in the seat and doesn't even spare the driver a glance. She is annoyed that he has not assisted by opening the door. Only when he says, "And where would madam wish to be taken?" does she realise that she is sitting beside a complete stranger. She has an excuse. It was the same colour as our car.

Another time I take her into town with me in the morning and as we part in the car park I say, "Remember, twelve o'clock prompt I'll be here to get home for my lunch." At twenty minutes past twelve she has not arrived so I drive home. She arrives home as I am about to drive back to work. "What happened?" I ask. Apparently she couldn't remember where we had parked and had wandered round for half an hour trying to locate the car. She cannot credit that I was unprepared to wait for her.

Decorating a room is something we do quite happily together. I really enjoy it. I like to make a start right after tea and this I can do if Joan has measured out several lengths of paper in advance. While she is clearing up the tea, I can get the paste prepared and my tools at the ready. It works best if she supports the paper and folds it up as I paste each section. I am up the stepladder and she passes me the paper ready to hang. I'm not one to stop for a coffee break. I prefer to get on with the job. We stop at about half-past ten so I manage a little look at the paper while Joan washes the tea dishes and makes the supper. After supper I'm ready for my bed but Joan always seems to have to stay up late getting schoolwork corrected. I don't understand why she doesn't enjoy the decorating as much as I do.

She says she thinks DIY is the reason why most marriages break up.

On one occasion we were putting a kind of bubble Anaglypta on the ceiling of the living room. As usual Joan had cut the lengths in advance. When it was pasted Joan had to keep it supported on one side of the ceiling while I brushed it across. I ended up on the other side with a couple of feet of paper to spare. Obviously all the paper has been incorrectly measured and cut. I supervise the measuring and cutting of the next batch only to find that when it is pasted we meet with the same difficulty. This bubble paper expands as it is pasted. I don't think we will be papering any more ceilings.

I'm no good at heights so when we are papering the well of the staircase I lay planks across and Joan is the one to balance on the planks, holding the top of each length of paper and letting it drop for me to brush it on. She manages pretty well.

CHAPTER
SEVEN

1964

For a long while we have considered letting Jenny sit the entrance exam for the grammar school, a grant-aided school which caters for both primary and secondary pupils. Some of our neighbours entered the names of their children for this school, which admits pupils at the ages of five, nine or eleven, as they were born. Joan said we would let Jenny wait to try for secondary admission. If she did not then pass the entrance exam, then she obviously would not benefit from attending such a school.

When her friend, Eleanor, sat for the nine-year-old entrance exam, Jenny suggested that she might do likewise but we talked her out of the idea. Later Jenny reported to us that when, at the interview following the exam, Eleanor was asked what she wanted to do when she grew up, her answer had been "I want to be a teacher". Just for fun Joan asked Jenny what she would have answered if asked the same question. Jenny's reply came without any hesitation, "Oh, Eleanor just said that because her mother told her to say it. I'd have told the truth. I'd have said I wanted to be a cinema usherette."

I'm not sure how Jenny would manage as a cinema usherette if it involved going up in the balcony. I guess she has inherited my fear of heights because although she is willing to occupy a seat in the balcony, nothing will induce her to approach the usherette as she stands with her back to the stalls below. Jenny would rather do without the ice cream. In the last two years she has managed to conquer her fear of the school stairs, which curve round to enclose the well below. Up to the age of eight she refused to carry any message to a teacher in an upstairs classroom.

This year Jenny will be eleven. Her birthday is December and she is only in Primary VI when, at the age of ten, she sits the exam in March and as a result is called for an interview at the grammar school. The headmistress says, "You are very young to start a secondary course." Jenny, wishing to accommodate, says, "Well, I don't mind if you put me in Primary VII. That is where my friend, Eleanor Brown, will be after the summer." Joan reckons Miss McKay may not take too kindly to being told what to do by a prospective pupil.

Despite Joan's fears, Jenny starts secondary school at the grammar at the end of August. Each night, after the tea is cleared she settles down to her homework on the dining table. She enjoys all the work she is set to do and is very conscientious. It is all finished before she goes to bed about nine o'clock. It is only then that I feel free to put on the television. We have storage heaters on the ground floor but none upstairs, so Jenny cannot be expected to work in her bedroom but, not for the first time, I think had we known we would be a family of four we might have been wiser to consider paying the extra cost of a bigger house.

One teatime Joan tells me she has been talking to a neighbour who invited her round to see a kitchen extension they have built out on the back wall of their original kitchen, thus creating an extra room. I say, "I could be interested in that idea." The neighbours who did this are kind enough to tell us some of the pitfalls which they encountered. Plans are drawn up and, having finally been granted building permission, I use a joiner, a plasterer and an electrician, all employed by Simpson and Shaw to work on company premises, to extend the business.

The men work most evenings through the spring of 1966, and I work alongside them as a labourer, stacking bricks and mixing cement. To try to preserve the light in the old kitchen they build in two walls of window in the extension. Joan also requests a perspex roof. They warn us that under such a roof we will fry in summer and freeze in winter. The joiner says, "I'll lay the necessary roof beams in case you change your minds after a year."

Joan asks the electrician to install a storage heater in what will become our dining room, telling him that we'll be opening up the sliding glass door and hatch window to allow the heat into the kitchen when we need it. The workmen shake their heads. "We'll be giving you a good seal on both the door and the hatch so you can keep the heat in your dining room and shut off the arctic temperature of your kitchen." The

71

workmen turn out to be right. Through that summer Joan is stripping off to cook the tea, while the following winter the dishcloth freezes during the night and is still a solid block when Joan comes home in the late afternoon. After one year we get the workmen back and a solid roof is put on the extension.

We are very happy with our new kitchen now. The joiner has created a beautiful storage unit to occupy one complete wall. It has a let-down flap for Joan to do her baking. A built-in table sits below the wall-length window overlooking the back garden and kitchen surfaces all have a formica finish. Our sink-unit now faces onto the hatch window, looking into our new dining room and beside it is housed the twin-tub washing machine. From Simpson and Shaw we have bought the four chrome dining chairs for when we eat in the kitchen and they have made us new kitchen curtains. While we are away on holiday the joiner lines the dining room walls with laminated wood panels so that when we return our Beith dining suite goes out of the front room and we have the equivalent of a five-apartment house. Now that we are no longer throwing toys into cardboard boxes or bathing babies in front of the fire, we have a room which might correctly be termed a sitting room.

It is just as we achieve all this that Joan tells me one of the neighbours is selling her piano very cheaply. She says, "Jenny has always wanted to learn piano. The violin was just a compromise because we had no room for a piano." I am horrified. "Over my dead body. We haven't just cleared space in the sitting room to clutter it with somebody's old piano." Joan argues that I am being unreasonable, but I stand firm. Finally I am forced to say, "Do what you like about the piano but I'll tell you this; the day that piano comes in here I'll be moving out." Joan repeats the choice of piano or Papa to Jenny. We do not buy the piano.

CHAPTER
EIGHT

Since I last changed my car we have started taking holidays further afield. This year we have booked into a hotel in Boscombe, just along the coast from Bournemouth. Only a car park separates us from the beach which is our regular morning destination. Scott is content to dig in the sand and fill his bucket at the edge of the waves. Jenny, who is able to swim, spends all her time in the sea. She urges us to join her. Joan is willing enough to spend some time with her, leaping on to the powerful breakers and letting the waves carry them in and out. I prefer to sit in a deck chair with a newspaper, having a bit of shut-eye and only stirring myself to collect the daily chocolate bars and soft drinks from the beach kiosk. I am willing to teach them how to play cricket on top of the cliffs in the afternoons and we play crazy golf on the promenade after the evening meal.

I tell the children that, as a special treat, I have booked seats for an evening show to see Arthur Askey at the Bournemouth Pier theatre. I do not allow for the traffic jams which face us on the way nor the difficulty in parking when we arrive. I have to drop the family to go into the show and join them half an hour later. Our enjoyment is somewhat spoiled by the intense heat of the theatre plus the fact that in a queue of cars it takes ages to return to the hotel. When we offer the next evening outing the children tell us they would prefer to be left out of the treat.

Scott, especially, is pleased when I buy a large beach ball. At some time each day we are all throwing it to one another. Accidentally it is thrown too far into the sea and it is being carried out on the tide. Nothing will satisfy but I must swim out to retrieve it. I do this for the next ten minutes, urged on by the family. At the end of this time the ball is still as far beyond me so, to everyone's disappointment I swim back. I explain that it may be one thing to have the strength to reach the ball but it is quite another to ensure that I will have the stamina to swim back. It is my guess that there is a strong current beyond the coigns and certainly some areas of the beach bear the flags signalling that it is unsafe to bathe. All ends well when a little later the lifeguard is passing in his boat and responds to our appeal to collect our ball.

It is the following year and we are back in Boscombe. Joan's sister, Thelma is with us and she is perfectly happy to paddle with Scott while Joan plays in the breakers with Jenny so I alternately read or doze. I'm wakened to a great disturbance on the beach. Four male holidaymakers are dragging two lilos to shore. On them there are two prone figures. As they are laid on the sand I see Joan, now sitting up, coughing and spluttering while the lad who had been brought in on the second lilo recovers almost immediately and moves off. People appear from all directions with flasks of hot tea and soup. Thelma, standing beside Jenny, is trying to calm her down. I am told the story.

Joan and Jenny were leaping on the breakers and letting themselves be carried out from the shore. Only when Joan tried to swim back did she find that with each renewed effort she was being taken further out of her depth. She could see the coigns and felt herself being carried in that direction, just as last year we had seen this happen to the beach ball. She shouted to Jenny to get me but instead Jenny was herself making vain attempts to reach her mother. In her panic she was screaming and it was her screams which alerted a young lad who swam out to help Joan. He was able to hold on to her but unable to prevent her head from going underwater. As she passed out at this point he could no longer cope and it was left to the men with the lilos to rescue them both. I say, "That's the last time we are coming on holiday to swim in the sea. From now on we'll find a place with a swimming pool."

We do not realise what a close thing this has been until we discover later that two guests from our hotel had drowned the previous summer. Although we see so many holidaymakers in the water with paddle boats and lilos, they are all taking great care not to get out of their depth.

When it comes to planning our holiday the following year, we spend an entire evening studying the brochures, trying to find a place to match all our requirements. We are still undecided when I retire to bed leaving Joan and Jenny still continuing the search.

76

When I come down next morning they tell me they have found the ideal spot in Totnes, near enough to both Paignton and Torquay. They show me a photograph of a large Elizabethan house standing in its own estate, complete with open-air swimming pool, tennis court, table tennis films shows and restaurant.

"And what," I ask, "is all this going to cost and who is going to provide the cash to pay it?"

"It is no more expensive than the other places we've looked at. It is a country club all the year round but open to summer visitors. The house has been converted into apartments where we cook our own meals."

"Well, there's no way I'm taking your Mum on holiday to cook meals just as she does every day when we are at home."

"But, Dad, we hate having to get back to the hotel in time for meals. We hate the time spent eating a huge lunch and a huge evening meal. We would settle for picnics. We don't care whether or not Mum cooks on holiday."

"I don't think it is going to work but if you all want it that way we'll book the first week in this Nine Elms place and we'll book the second week in the hotel at Goodwin Sands which is my choice."

Travelling on the busy roads at the Glasgow Fair, it takes us forever to reach Totnes, the last lap of the drive taking us through the high-hedged Devon lanes which are so narrow that you have to pull into the verge to let another car pass. I am tired and I am cross, and when we are still on the road at eight o'clock I give voice to my frustration, "I'll tell you this; once we get there you'd best be satisfied with the place. I won't be driving these lanes again until the day we leave." We are the only ones dining in the restaurant and they don't serve anything as mundane as the sausage and chips which Scott always chooses. It is not until the next morning that we discover we have picked a winner.

We are in a large ground-floor apartment where the children just step out of the French windows to reach the swimming pool. Everyone congregates at the pool. It becomes the equivalent of the public lounge in a conventional hotel. The other guests are extremely sociable, many of them renewing acquaintance from former holidays. On the premises there's a bar alongside the restaurant, a coffee bar, a shop selling chocolate, soft drinks, ice cream, and cigarettes. Outside the shop there are a couple of slot machines yielding prizes of cash tokens which can be spent in the shop.

Scott is intrigued by the prospect of increasing his pocket money in such an easy way. He is desolate when he loses his first sixpence. Joan is about to compensate the loss but I point out that if she does, he is going to miss out on a valuable lesson. As it is he won't be in a hurry to try his luck again. In the grounds there is a tennis court where the three of us can assure ourselves that we are not among the worst players, and one day there is a tennis tournament where we join the spectators to watch some great tennis from some of the regular guests. On the terrace there are facilities for playing table-tennis plus a separate building housing a games room with more table-tennis and snooker tables.

One day the guests organise their own treasure hunt and one evening we have an amateur talent contest. The family proprietors organise film shows a couple of nights a week. We watch the Doris Day comedies. We have to sit and wait while the reels are changed which all adds to the fun.

The restaurant is frequently as empty as it was the night of our arrival as most people prefer to order the bar meals. The family prepare all the meals in advance and these are quickly re-heated in an invention I've never come across before. It is called a microwave oven. We collect our chicken or scampi baskets and Joan is having to do very little cooking.

Scott, who is not usually keen to make friends on short acquaintance, joins a group going out for the day in a fishing boat. That day he provides the fish which Joan cooks for our supper. It's true she also nearly sets the house on fire as she attempts to cook chips in a shallow frying pan. She copes with dousing the flames before other guests, passing by our windows have time to raise the alarm.

Jenny is having a wonderful time in the pool at every opportunity along with a Dutch family and several teenagers. There's a table set apart for them outside the bar where they can enjoy soft drinks and be part of the company.

One morning, two young men knock on the door of our apartment and are engaged in some sort of apology. There's a good deal of laughing before Joan closes the door after them.

"What was all that about?" I ask.

"Well, it was last night after we had come in to go to bed. You were already asleep and I was half-undressed when the French windows were opened and these two men stepped into the room."

"It could have been anyone. Why didn't you waken me?"

"Because it all happened so quickly. No one spoke a word. They just crossed the room and went out of the door on the other side. I didn't know it then but they have just explained that they had been out for the evening, had come back late to find the main door locked and presumed that, because it is on the ground floor they had found a way in through one of the public rooms."

"But you were half undressed."

"That's what all the laughing was about. They said they were looking for me to present their apology but were not sure that they could recognise me fully clothed which was why they decided to knock on our door."

I give up. It seems there is no end to the odd situations Joan gets herself into. I'm learning not to be surprised by anything.

We are heartbroken to be leaving at the end of the week and the hotel in Goodwin Sands is more than a bit of an anti-climax. By contrast to our earlier week it seems so stuffy and formal. People are friendly enough and Joan and Jenny swim before lunch with other guests who assure them that this has to be the safest place to swim in the British Isles. When the tide is high they only have to go out through the garden to reach the bay. Joan says the water is of such density that it holds you up and you can convince yourself that you are a champion swimmer.

All the male visitors are anxious to see a particular football game on TV so Joan says she will take the children into Torquay by bus. They want to see *Born Free* and if they are to see the film from the beginning they will have to miss the evening meal. Jenny and Scott are delighted at the idea of missing out on the second large meal of the day. From now on we are hooked on self-catering and several subsequent holidays find us back in Nine Elms.

On one of these holidays Joan and I go out for lunch one day with friends, leaving Scott beside the pool. It is a wet day, so the pool is deserted. Scott, put off by the near drowning episode at Boscombe and later by the fact that he was to become trapped under a lilo in a swimming pool, is reluctant to do other than splash around in the shallow end of the pool. Many times we have tried to encourage him and failed. In our absence on this particular morning two men whom he has only met at these holidays succeed where we have failed. When we return from lunch we are treated to a demonstration of Scott swimming the length of the pool. This achievement pays off dividends in Scott's whole attitude from that day onwards. It is as if he needed that boost to give himself the confidence that he so lacked.

We are to continue visiting Totnes until Scott is in his early teens. On our last holiday there he pals up with the daughter of the proprietor who instructs him in the judicial bit of manoeuvring and shaking of the machines which will result in a regular win. There's little I can do about this fraudulent behaviour but I am to remember it well some years later.

CHAPTER
NINE

At the end of her second school year at the grammar school, Jenny is presented with the class prize and she is also awarded a bursary which is to pay her fees for the rest of her schooldays. We now consider Scott. Unlike Jenny, the only books Scott is interested in are about wheels and levers. He is a regular reader of *Dandy* and *Beano* and saves all his pocket money to buy additions to his Hornby train set. With him apparently lacking Jenny's flair for learning, we fear that it might be unwise to bank all hopes of Scott getting into the boys' grammar on the eleven-year-old entrance. We decide to let him try when he is nine years old so that, if he is successful, he will enter the primary school for Standards VI and VII.

Scott does pass the entrance examination but is very unhappy during his first week. It is day two of the new school when not only does he get on the wrong train and has to walk home from King's Park, but for homework he has to correct all the sums marked wrong in class. Joan takes a look at his original answers, finds they are all correct and asks Scott who had done the marking. He says that the teacher told them to exchange books with a neighbouring pupil before dictating the answers. These answers are in hundreds of thousands and evidently the boy who marked Scott's got lost on the oral notation. She explains to Scott that he must point this out to the teacher next day. Even so Scott insists on doing all the sums again.

On day three Scott comes home from school and tells us a tale of how a boy in his class was refused permission to leave the room and was sick all over the floor. He says he feels sick and what will happen if he goes back to school and the same thing happens to him. We say if he is sick he had best stay at home the next day. The following evening we suggest that as he has not been sick he will be fit to go to school the next morning. Later we hear him crying in bed. At last he confesses he hates the school where everything has to be done at the double and the class teacher is very strict.

Joan says, "Maybe you'll be happier back at Limewood."

"What about the school uniform you've had to pay for?"

"That's not a problem."

Scott looks relieved, "Will you write a letter?"

"Oh, I don't think so", Joan says casually. "It's only fair that you should tell the headmaster why you are leaving."

"What will he say?"

"Well, he might say a week is not very long to judge."

"Perhaps I should give it another week."

"That seems a good idea. I've a suggestion for you. You told us all the things you don't like. Let's suppose that tomorrow you try to find one thing that makes it okay."

At home after school the following day Scott announces that two good things had happened at school. The first of these is that he now has a pal, having found someone to share a giggle in the music lesson and secondly, Mr Thomas had called him Scott.

"What did he call you before?"

"He just called me 'that big lad at the back'."

Joan's comment: "There's a lesson for every teacher in that."

So Scott struggles on and he is quite happy when he comes second to bottom of the class. We console ourselves that he is not very bright, so it is a surprise to us when we receive Scott's final primary report card indicating that Scott has not only achieved a praiseworthy position in class but that Mr. Thompson's comment written beneath declares, "Scott should always be in the top ten pupils of any class".

Scott moves into secondary school and gets by with the minimum of work, while Jenny plays in the school orchestra and each year walks away with all the glittering prizes.

Saturday afternoons when I am at work, Jenny and her friend, Helen, go down to the local café or just sit around the house with girlie magazines. I walk in one day to find them standing at the gate, sporting stick-on eyelashes painted silver and gold. They bat them at me as I pass. I say to Joan, "I'm not too happy about the girls standing outside wearing those ridiculous eyelashes. Where did they get them?" Joan is unperturbed. "They are only paper eyelashes they have cut out of a magazine. It's harmless enough, Alex. They are just growing up." She says the same thing when I complain about the posse of lanky lads who hang around the gate. I say, "It's like dogs round a bone. Can't they find somewhere else to stand?"

"You mean outside someone else's gate? I don't think we can encourage that."

The final straw is the mini-skirt. I can't believe Joan allows her to wear such an indecent garment. Joan says she is doing her best but Jenny has a Saturday job now and how she spends her money is her own affair. Jenny's first job is working on a Saturday morning in a shoe shop in the town. For this she is paid one pound. She drives in and out with me to save bus fares.

I say, "It's sheer exploitation, sometimes she makes ten sales during the morning. We're talking a hundred pounds worth of goods and she comes away with one pound."

"Do you want her to chuck it in?"

"Oh, no. It's a good thing she is finding out how little such jobs pay. Hopefully she'll want to go in for a more rewarding career."

One year, at Nine Elms, Jenny chums up with a young man, Don, aged about nineteen. He tells her he will be in Glasgow for a family wedding later in August and asks if he may come to see her. I'm surprised when he actually turns up one day and Jenny is invited to accompany him to the wedding. Apparently Don has asked if he may stay at our house after the wedding, when his parents have returned home. One evening Don and Jenny go to the local cinema and it is nearly eleven o'clock when they get home. While we are waiting for them to come in, I am watching the clock, "I'm not having them coming in at this time. Does he know she is only fourteen? You deal with Jenny and I'll take him into the dining room and deal with him. If he thinks he is coming back here on Sunday after his parents go home he can think again. By the time I've finished with him he won't dare show his face again."

The following day is a Communion Sunday so, because I am now an Elder, I have to go out to church ahead of Joan. Before she leaves home she receives a telephone call from Don's mother asking if it is okay with us for Don to stay up in Glasgow for a couple more days. During the service Joan manages to convey most of this to me by a series of gestures across the pews which divide us. As a fellow Elder once put it, "There's nothing like communion for splitting up the family." Don is extremely polite and careful not to offend me during the rest of his stay. For Scott Don is something of a role model. He is obviously impressed by Don's satin quilted dressing gown. It is what Scott requests for his Christmas present that year. Joan manages to find one in a small men's size in Marks and Spencer's. It is supposed to be knee-length but it reaches Scott's feet. Scott, not yet twelve, wears it for the next ten years.

The mini-skirt is still in fashion when I come home from the office one day to find three or four of Jenny's friends sprawled round the sitting room. I join Joan in the kitchen, where she is cooking the tea.

"Don't you want to sit in an easy chair?" Joan asks.

"Yes, I do," I confess, "but whichever direction I look in, I find myself looking up a mini-skirt."

It is around this time that Jenny swops jobs to work a full Saturday in the local mini-market. This is much better paid but there are several snags. Jenny tells Joan that when the owner asks her to wash the storeroom floor she refuses. "I'm not doing that floor with all the creepy-crawlies," she says. "If you want it done you'll have to do it yourself." Jenny also mentions that, although he professes to be a strict Muslim who abstains from alcoholic drink, he is not past looking at pornographic pictures in magazines and attempting to engage her attention in them. Her reply to him on these occasions is "Keep your dirty pictures to yourself."

Joan reports these conversations to me, adding that maybe we should not be exposing Jenny to such behaviour. I say, "It sounds as if she is dealing with it well enough. She's a pretty girl and she is going to meet up with advances such as these for a long time to come. It seems a safe enough situation to me and it is an opportunity for her to learn how to cope. You make yourself known in the shop and I'll pop in from time to time myself so he is aware we are keeping an eye on him."

Some time later Jenny says, "He often goes into the back shop for a while and, it seems to me he deliberately leaves the till open to see if I help myself.

Again, at the end of the day he tells me to choose what I want from the shelves."

I tell her to point out to him occasionally that he has left the till open and to say that we forbid her to bring home goods she has not paid for. Jenny carries out these instructions and most Saturdays he rewards her honesty by topping up the pay.

On Saturday nights she and Helen go to a local disco and I pick them up when it closes. I feel this is a bit of an imposition on my half-day off but when I talk to a neighbouring parent he says, "You think you are badly done to when you have to collect your daughter. You should try it with a son. Most nights that I go to collect him I have to hang around while he says goodnight to his girlfriend."

I think that possibly this chore is about to end when, outside the church on Sunday morning Mrs Brown says, "I wouldn't allow my girls to attend that disco. I'm told they have bouncers on the door, frisking people for drink as they enter." Joan says, "If the bouncers ensure that it doesn't develop into a drunken brawl I'm all for it, myself."

CHAPTER
TEN

1968

Jenny tells us that her headmistress has suggested an interchange of pupils with a school in Germany, the idea being that we give hospitality to a German girl for three months and our daughter will later be looked after in a German home, an opportunity for both girls to practise their language skills. Svenja comes to stay. She is a very well-mannered girl and her English is quite good. She attends school with Jenny and manages to cope in most subjects with the exception of Latin so Joan writes to Miss McKay and Svenja is excused from these lessons. What drives us all up the wall is the two-hour session required to complete her ablutions in our one and only bathroom. Jenny thinks she puts rollers in her shoulder-length hair and doesn't come out until the curls have set.

She shares a room with Jenny, but tends to monopolise it. It seems she doesn't want to socialise with Jenny and Scott, preferring to put in an appearance only when Joan or I am around to correct her English. Jenny complains that she doesn't get any chance to practise her German. We suggest to Svenja that as a form of compromise she will speak English all day but in the bedroom at night she and Jenny will speak German. Svenja nods with her usual "Ja, ja", and smiles her agreement but never once in the following weeks does she honour her promise.

She has been here a fortnight when we discover that she has never written home. She says she is still writing the letter but has not yet got beyond describing the flight. We take Svenja trips to local holiday resorts and she enjoys accompanying Jenny and Helen to the Saturday discos. She asks Jenny, "What do I say if someone asks me to dance when I would not choose to dance with him?" Jenny's answer is, "Just say, 'Get lost'." Like me, Jenny does not believe in wasting words.

While Svenja is with us Jenny develops German measles, so for a week or so they are both excluded from school. We ask the doctor what precautions we can take for Svenja. His answer is: "None. She has probably already contracted the infection and if so you are doing her a favour. In fact, throw a party for all their friends. If they take German measles in their teens, it can avoid trouble later when they are expectant mothers". Svenja does not develop the illness, and the bathroom situation worsens by the day. Jenny and Scott are both thoroughly fed up with her shunning of their company. I say, "She is a guest in this house and must be treated accordingly." To save my own sanity I try to teach Svenja the meaning of the phrase "a lick and a promise".

As the end of June approaches we are all looking forward to our Devon summer holiday without Svenja.

The plan has always been that she would meet up down south with a friend to stay in a youth hostel in order to experience the "swinging London of the sixties".

It is at this point that we discover that Svenja has never written to the youth hostel to book her accommodation. Jenny is near to tears: "She's going to end up coming on holiday with us." It is Joan, now aware of Svenja's powers of procrastination, who writes the letter and secures the booking.

It is the night before Svenja's departure. She has packed the trunk which we are to send back to Germany and has spent all day taking things in and out of a suitcase for London. At bedtime she tells us that the case is so full it will not close. Joan repacks it, throwing out all the non-essentials, and manages to get it shut. Two hours later Svenja emerges from the bathroom with the bulging toilet bag in her hand, "to go in the case", she says. Joan is very firm: "We are not opening up that case again, Svenja, you will carry that bag in your hand."

For about five days while Svenja is with us, Ernest, a former curate-in-charge of the church Joan attended, comes from Toronto to stay with us. He is the last thing you'd expect in a reverend; a bit of a maverick I'd guess. He is now a professor of English. He spends much of his time with Jenny discussing music and playing duets with her on the piano.

Oh, yes, we now have a piano. About a year ago Dave and Enid were moving up to Perthshire to manage a hotel and they gifted us their piano. It takes up most of a whole wall but I'm prepared to suffer it. Now we learn from Ernest that it is a particularly good piano because of the way it is strung.

Joan has a throat infection but welcomes the break from school where, this year, she has a difficult class. She is terribly thin. While I am at work Ernest is happy to sit in the garden talking to Joan or to join her in their trips to the local supermarket or into town. In the town he insists on buying presents for everyone; a beautiful stamp album and a collection of stamps for Scott, two records for Jenny, one a recording of old church organ music and the other a medley of Simon and Garfunkel songs. For Svenja he buys a large talc and fluffy puff. He brought perfume for Joan and later, from South Africa, he sends me a piece of native craftwork. On the Saturday we leave the rest of the family behind and the three of us take a drive to Loch Katrine. We are all sorry to see him leave to stay with London friends.

Perhaps now Joan will catch up on some sleep. Ernest slept downstairs on the studio couch while he was here and, although I went up to my bed at about eleven o'clock, Ernest and Joan had another talking session until the early hours of the morning. One day I ask, "What time was it when you got to bed last night?" Joan appears to struggle to remember and finally says, "I'm not sure. It must have been after midnight." While Joan finds it very difficult to tell even a white lie, I'm well aware that she is a master of understatement. Essentially, I suppose she is a very open person and, from time to time this causes me some embarrassment. We might be planning a party to which I do not want to invite Neil, so I warn Joan to refrain from mentioning it next time he calls. I say, "You know what he's like. He'll insist on introducing one of his childish games like throwing a ball into a hat." Inevitably she lets slip the truth which I would have preferred unspoken.

We plan our annual parties with great enthusiasm. We hold them in the week between Christmas and New Year when Thelma is with us, and she is a wizard at producing all the sausage rolls, vol-au-vents and numerous cakes. The three of us spend a couple of days organising the entertainment. Our tape recorder provides us with much of the fun. We involve our guests in performing a potted version of the Morecambe and Wise TV show. Ralph performs his magic to the accompaniment of his excellent patter, and we always end up with Charades.

As a result of Svenja's stay with us, Jenny and Scott have developed a new closeness, bonded by their common resentment of Svenja's behaviour. Not so long ago we couldn't even leave them to do the washing-up together without it ending in a quarrel. When I gave Scott a ticking-off for resorting to physical combat, Joan said this was unjust in that without it he was no match for Jenny's tongue. Now, they share much secret humour, so the outcome of Svenja's visit has become quite positive.

The following year Jenny spends a month of her summer holiday staying with Svenja's family in Hamburg. On her return home she tells us how, at each meal, Svenja's father said, "Now we speak English", and how, throughout her stay, she was determined to do no such thing.

When, without Jenny, we go back to Nine Elms that summer, it is for the last time. Joan misses not having Jenny with us and we find that the family who used to run the establishment have sold it to a professional entertainer who looks on it as a profit-making hobby. For the next couple of years we try out self-catering accommodation in North Devon where there are fewer tourists and we meet less-congested roads. We like North Devon but as far as good company goes the holidays do not come up to the standard of Nine Elms.

Towards the end of the summer term Jenny sat her Highers, and the results arrive while she is in Germany. On her instructions the envelope stays sealed until her return. She sat Highers in English, Maths, Latin, French, German and Spanish, and she has achieved the top level in all subjects. She has sent away all the UCCA forms applying to Oxford, Cambridge and Glasgow and on the strength of her success in Highers receives an unconditional acceptance from all three. Meanwhile she is back at school for a sixth year to pursue some A levels.

When Oxford is put down as her first choice, I ask, "What can you learn at Oxford that you can't learn at Glasgow where you could still live at home? Think of the extra expense it will involve for us to let you to go to Oxford." Joan tells Jenny to talk to her headmistress about Oxford fees and we discover that, although with both parents earning Jenny will only qualify for the minimum student grant, our parental contribution will be the same regardless of where she chooses to study. So Jenny sits the Oxford and Cambridge entrance examinations and, in December of 1970, as she reaches her seventeenth birthday, she is selected for interviews.

It is the winter of discontent in Britain. As Prime Minister, Edward Heath puts service industries and businesses on part-time rather than give in to the unions, with the result that there is a different strike breaking out each week. Our life is curtailed by power cuts and on the day Jenny is to fly to Oxford for the interview we are in the middle of a bread strike in Scotland. A day or two before Jenny's flight, a letter arrives requesting her attendance at Cambridge for an interview later the same day. Joan rings Miss McKay, who says she will contact Cambridge and arrange for Jenny to travel on from Oxford a day later. Jenny returns, pretty sure that she prefers Oxford and having remembered to bring us a loaf.

A week later we are informed by both of the colleges to which she applied that she has been successful in the interviews, with the additional offer from Oxford of a scholarship. I harbour my doubts about this Oxford business but I'm proud to be able to go into the office and report her success to a couple of my close colleagues. I hope all this proof of her ability does not go to her head. She has always been very argumentative. If I check her for any misbehaviour she can never just accept it. There has to be a confrontation. In my opinion this is the reason I am failing to teach her to handle a car. For an apparently brilliant pupil she fails miserably in trying to grasp how and at which point to get the car started.

Of course, Joan was the same when I tried to teach her to drive some years ago. She was paying for some lessons at the local driving school soon after we obtained our second car. She told me that the instructor said the lessons alone were useless if she wasn't getting some practice in between so, against my better judgement, I agreed to take her to a nearby trading estate where she could learn in safety. I made the mistake of asking if she wanted to drive the car over to the site. We hadn't travelled a hundred yards down the hill at the foot of the avenue when she put the car into neutral and we hit the nearest lamp-post. The front radiator was damaged so we had to accept a tow home from a driver who was passing. He spent the rest of the evening in our house, perhaps fearing what kind of a scene might take place if he left us alone. Joan seemed unhurt and surprised to think that just easing into a lamp-post could have such a disastrous effect while I spent my time going to and fro to the bathroom being physically sick.

She agreed that, once we had paid the seventy pounds for the repair and had the car back in use, it would be foolish to risk another accident when we needed the car to reach our holiday destination but she did complete the driving course. After the holiday, Dave, an office colleague of mine, took her out in the car every Sunday afternoon for several weeks. He suggested that I should accompany them on the last of these outings so I might witness Joan's remarkable progress. I was told to sit in the back seat and to refrain from making comments. Well, I certainly had to comment as Joan put the car into motion. "What about checking the driving mirrors and what about hand signals?" From that moment on, Joan crashed every gear change and I feared for the damage she was inflicting on my car.

For the weeks that followed I persevered when it was possible to let her take the wheel. She was hopeless. She was unable to respond promptly to traffic lights, road conditions or the actions of other drivers. I was forced to tell her this again and again. More than once she left the car in a huff, telling me she would rather walk than sit in the car next to me. She did this once in the middle of the Fenwick moors. I don't know how she thought she would get home from that deserted spot. Finally I said, "I can't ever see you becoming a good driver. In Glasgow, if you're not a good driver you'll be a dead driver, and I've got a vested interest in keeping you alive." Joan gave up the driving after that and now, it seems, Jenny has similarly decided.

It is Saturday evening and I have taken an early bath and I'm relaxing in pyjamas and dressing gown watching TV when the phone rings. It is Jenny. Please can I go into town to collect her and her friends since they have missed the last bus and are unable to get a taxi. I slam down the phone and very irritated and with many protests I set about re-dressing.

Joan says, "You shouldn't complain, Alex. She is only doing what you have always told her to do. Again and again you have warned her about accepting a lift from a stranger."

"She should have made sure she caught the bus."

"I agree but if she didn't and she can't get a taxi she has done the right thing phoning home."

"You are always making excuses for her, always taking her side against me. Parents are supposed to be on the same side."

Having dropped off her friends, I give Jenny a piece of my mind. To conclude I add, "Your behaviour causes quarrels between your Mum and me. Is that what you want?" Jenny arrives home in tears and, leaving the pair of them, I get myself to bed. Joan does not come up until some time later when I am already asleep. It must be the one and only time we have ever slept on a quarrel.

The family are already at breakfast when I join them on the Sunday morning. I say, "I've had a bit of time to think over what happened last night. I was upset then but you did right to phone, Jenny. I was wrong and I am sorry."

This is to be our last summer holiday with Jenny before she leaves home to live in Oxford. We are to drive to North Devon with a packed car because we are taking Thelma and Jenny's friend, Moira, with us. To make this possible I construct a seat for Scott between the two front passenger seats. This means I do not have access to the handbrake and three people are going to be cramped in the back but I intend to drive very carefully. As it turns out, the traffic is even heavier than usual at the Fair and we are often travelling at a snail's pace. It is a hot day, and many cars with overheated engines break down and block the main roads. Once we get clear of Bristol we are glad to take a break. We go to a pub for a sandwich but for the first time we discover ploughman's lunch and from then on we actually seek out pubs when we are on holiday.

On that holiday we spend an afternoon in Westward Ho! and we even find a second-hand bookshop where Jenny is able to buy many of the prescribed books for her English course. I really miss Jenny during the terms when she is away from home and I miss the young people who visited us when she lived at home. I don't particularly miss the various short-lived boyfriends. In my opinion the lads of today have no idea of making themselves look smart when they are taking a girlfriend out for the evening. They are a pack of long-haired layabouts. I don't think one of them possesses a suit. I express this opinion to Jenny. I say, "What happened to Tom? He had some appearance and good manners." "You just liked Tom because he called you 'sir' and the reason I don't go out with him any more is because the police caught him with drugs. So much for your well-mannered young man." Not that Jenny looks a whole lot smarter herself. She has the advantage of having been born with good looks and could really make something of herself if she tried, but since she has been at Oxford she wears long, droopy skirts, her hair down to her shoulders and a coat that reaches her ankles. Round the house she wears a black crocheted waistcoat that flaps round her knees. She stood at the door one day as we drove off, looking like some waif begging on the streets. I said to Joan, "Ryan's Daughter!"

One vacation we have a visit from Jake, the current boyfriend from Oxford. His wardrobe is enhanced by an ankle-length, ex-army greatcoat bought for a song from the army and navy surplus store. I catch a glimpse of them setting off for the cinema as I turn into the drive. I ask Joan which film they are going to see.

She says, "*Nicholas and Alexandra*, I think."

"They're certainly dressed appropriately. They look like a couple of Russian revolutionaries."

When we visit Jenny in her last year at Oxford there's a boyfriend called Martin. The two of them are sharing a flat along with other pals. We meet them one Saturday morning when, loaded on to a wheelbarrow, they have a moth-eaten couch which they are delivering to the flat. While we are away for our holiday that summer, Martin is staying with Jenny and Scott in Glasgow but we don't even see him. He has left earlier on the day that they knew we were returning home.

Jenny's time at Oxford ends with yet another of the "glittering prizes" — a double first in English — so she plans to continue studying for a doctorate. Apparently the parental contribution is at an end and she is entitled to a further grant. I can't think why she wants to go on penniless when she could get a well-paid job. She is living in Oxford still, boarding with one of her married women tutors.

In the December of this year, having reached her twenty-first birthday she shows us a ring she is wearing; a present from Martin. She points out to us that she is wearing the ring on her engagement finger, although she stresses that they do not want the news broadcast. I am in a dilemma. How am I supposed to participate in their apparent joy if I am not allowed to share the news with my family, friends and neighbours? I can only hope it will be some considerable time before they contemplate marriage.

I am wrong. It turns out they want to get married in May, in Oxford, and just with close family and Oxford friends. I think they are both being very foolish. Martin intends going back to study for a second degree next October but in order to be accepted he is planning to work for a year. I say, "How am I supposed to organise a wedding service and reception from Glasgow?" only to be told that it will be a registry office wedding and they will arrange it all themselves.

They do. My hopes of a proud moment walking down the aisle with my only daughter disappear. It seems all we have to do is to drive down with Martin's parents so that we will together arrive in Oxford for a noon wedding. The reception is to be in a small hotel, inappropriately called the Dorchester. The only cars belong to the parents. The bride and groom walk together to the registry office, while American tourists who happen to be in the area smile indulgently, commenting, "Say, honey, don't they make a real cute pair." The guests get themselves to the reception on their bicycles.

The "ceremony" is over in ten minutes, but the reception is a great success. We are thanked effusively by all the guests (I suppose I did provide the cash) who tell us that, given the choice, this would be the kind of wedding and reception which they would undoubtedly prefer, except their parents would raise too many objections. We wave the newly married couple off on

102

their honeymoon — a one-night stay in a hotel followed by a week living in a tent. Not my idea of a honeymoon, but then it was circumstances rather than penury which prevented us from having any kind at all. One of the hotel staff comments that Martin looked "like the cat that's got the cream" and I agree.

CHAPTER
ELEVEN

Joan is now doing part-time remedial teaching at a local secondary school. Last year she resigned from primary teaching. She had accepted a promotion to a school as assistant head in charge of all but the infant classes. It was not easy to get there by public transport and Joan wasn't prepared for the conditions in which her days were spent on administration with less and less teaching. She was more miserable than I'd ever seen her, continually frustrated over the trivial demands made on her time and in despair at her inability to deal with the whole situation. I told her in no uncertain terms that I didn't want to come home each night to listen to a catalogue of her woes and to go to bed on my own, leaving her working at schemes which vainly she hoped might meet with the head's approval. I said, "You know, when we got married I was under the illusion that couples at least went to bed at the same time."

For a couple of weeks Joan was off school and attending the doctor. Her weight had dropped below eight stone and the doctor put her on tranquillisers. I said, "Why you go on, I don't know. You don't have to go out to work. We can get by without your earnings.

Cut your losses and get out." So Joan resigned and for a whole six months she was just at home, dispensed with the Valium and made a full recovery. So much so that when the newly appointed headmaster of Kingston Park invited her to become his remedial teacher on a part-time basis she jumped at it.

Life is not without its difficulties and Scott is difficulty number one. His main interest lies in getting jobs to supplement his pocket money. He delivers cream on Friday nights and Saturday mornings. Prior to that he had attended the Boys' Brigade meetings on Friday nights. I had been an active member of the BB when I was young and I had enjoyed it. Scott made no secret of the fact that he hated it. He complained that when he spent every day of the week at school in school uniform, the last thing he wanted to do on the only night with no homework was to get into another uniform of the itchy jersey and to be subject to a kind of discipline which was worse than school. So he has chucked the BB and we ourselves suggested that it might be to everyone's advantage if he also stopped attending the youth group of the church which went under the name of Youth Pilgrims. Joan had accidentally discovered that Scott, along with his friend, Derek, spent their time there causing as much disruption as they could manage, much to the detriment of the enterprise and the leader's aspirations.

On his regular cream run he can earn a bonus if he sells all the cream in his pack. He manages to do this most weeks, selling the last four or six cartons to Joan at a reduced price, a reduction he can manage to fund while still gaining from the bonus payment. Where money is concerned Scott is very capable of putting his mind to work. When he was regularly spending every penny he earned I suggested to him that by banking some of it he could gain from the interest. Now he sees the interest credited to his bankbook he banks every penny he can.

"He never brings you in so much as a bar of chocolate," I complain to Joan. "He has to learn to spend as well as save."

"I expect he thinks his contribution would be a bit surplus", says Joan. "I've had a box of chocolates from you every weekend since we have been married."

As usual Joan's mother is staying with us for most of July. Scott comes in one day with the record of Frank Sinatra's *My Way*. He has no record player of his own but he borrows Jenny's machine and we hear it played continuously. Joan's mother's comment is, "I think he is trying to tell us something."

A subject I frequently raise with Scott is how ridiculously extravagant it is to have an hour's telephone conversation with a pal who lives two minutes away, especially when neither of them is footing the phone bill. Wasting electricity is another topic I pursue. There are lights left on all over the house and a fan heater burning in his bedroom when he could just as easily do his work downstairs beside a storage heater. Unlike Jenny, Scott pays great heed to me when I am urging him to change his ways. Always for the following week there is a change in his

106

behaviour. It is a great pity that usually he fails to sustain this change.

I have actually to seek him out to conduct these talks. He remains in his room where, under the pretence of working, he has nodded off or he is entertaining his friends so that when the door is opened the smell of burning joss sticks make you think it is some dive in Soho. I only see him at meal times and I can tell you I was pretty shocked the other day when he said life would be perfect if only we could install a dumb waiter that would serve his meals directly to his room.

Sometimes he announces that he is staying up to see the late film on television and Joan sits up with him. I ask her why she should choose to keep him company when it is not her type of film and he seldom speaks a word. Her answer to that is, "The chances are he'll pass some remark during the commercial breaks." In fact very often, just as the film is about to begin there's a knock on the door. After Scott has opened it to his pal Steve, he pops back long enough to announce that he is going to watch the film at Steve's house and nobody need wait up as he has remembered his key. Joan says, "You mean you are going to Steve's now, after midnight? Why? Steve can watch the film here".

"Mum, it's a colour TV in Steve's house. Here we have only just bought a set that shows BBC 2."

When I was young I played most forms of sport. I'm not trying to pretend I was championship standard at any but, whether it was tennis or golf or snooker, I could play well enough to enjoy it and not spoil anyone else's game. It surprises me that Scott has no interest in any sport whatever. He saved up to buy his own bike but I don't think he has ever gone further than a mile on it. He and Derek seem to spend a fair bit of their time just making mischief. I came home last Saturday having worked a full day to hear what had ensued during the afternoon. Scott had apparently told Joan that a man who lived round the corner was accusing him and Derek of deliberately hanging around outside his house to peer in the windows and he was threatening to report them to the police. Joan had gone round to this man's house only to come up against a very angry individual using the most profane language.

I listened to this tale but when Joan suggested that I go round to face the person concerned I shook my head.

"But he swore at me. Aren't you willing to back me up?"

"Certainly not. If I go to see him I could end up losing my temper. I could hit him and then I'd be in trouble. You've done well to have it out with him without any shots being fired. It's probably all over nothing."

It is weeks later when we hear that this man obviously suffers from a persecution complex. The boys are not the only people he has reported to the police. He has been warned by them that if he makes any more false accusations he will be penalised for wasting police time. Even so, I cannot believe that Scott and Derek are entirely innocent of causing some kind of provocation deliberately to goad him into losing his temper.

108

There's another Saturday when I discover Scott has got himself into some real trouble. It is over an incident that occurred during a holiday with his pal, John. We had relented into agreeing that the boys be allowed to spend a week of their holiday in Millport. It is later that summer, when Joan is ironing in the kitchen, that Scott goes through to tell her that two C.I.D. men are waiting to speak to her. "It's over a bit of trouble in Millport," he adds.

The police are making enquiries about a letter, written on solicitor's notepaper, which has been forwarded to them by the proprietor of an amusement arcade in Millport. They produce the letter for Joan to read. The letter, as if written by some legal representative, accuses the proprietor of a physical assault on the person of John Morley, giving time, date etc., and signed Scott Park with home address. Scott admits composing the letter and says it was sent because this man had demanded that the boys leave the amusement arcade after he had accused them of tampering with the machines. When they denied this and refused to leave, he had struck John. Although no physical retaliation took place, the boys later planned to cause him some degree of discomfort by letting him think that they had reported the assault.

"How did they get hold of the legal notepaper?" is what the inspectors are most anxious to discover. Scott then has to admit that it was their mutual friend, Derek, whose father is a solicitor, who appropriated the notepaper without permission. "You see," says one of the policemen, "quite evidently this was a revenge cruelly and calculatedly planned." Joan says she may be able to account for this if Scott is sent out of the room. She then proceeds to tell them how Scott has twice been cheated into sending off both foreign stamps and later musical recordings in answer to magazine advertisements promising reimbursements which were never honoured. Now, when he deals with post of any kind, he signs himself as Scott Park Esquire, giving himself a status other than his own. She concludes with, "While other boys might have had a go at beating up the proprietor, Scott and John planned this as a stupid kind of joke."

"Except they are not stupid boys," is the police response to this. "They attend a grammar school, proving that they must be pretty bright."

"So bright," Joan argues, "that they add a home address to the letter."

From then on it becomes evident that the chief concern of the police in this matter is to trace the notepaper. The boys are to be let off with a warning and it is Derek's father who is to be questioned on how it came about that the notepaper was lying around in his house. When I get home and hear this story I am livid, and I tell Scott what I think about him in no uncertain terms. "I hope you realise that your name will be on police files from this day on. If you ever want to emigrate it is going to be considered as a blot on your character. I wonder what neighbours will think seeing a police car outside the house and two policemen gaining entrance. Do you have no consideration for the rest of your family? And what about Derek's father? How will we all feel if on account of this he loses his job?"

Joan later reminds me that as far as the neighbours are concerned it wasn't a police car and the men were in plain clothes. She agrees that Scott has to go round and apologise to Derek's dad but then she says a very odd thing, "That letter they let me read — it was really well-constructed in good English. I never dreamt that Scott could put sentences together as well as that."

It seems that hardly a day goes by but what Scott gives me some anxiety. It is December and Joan has cooked a roast chicken. She says we won't be having chicken again this side of Christmas so we can better enjoy a week of eating turkey at Christmas. As we sit down to our evening meal, I open the post which Joan has left by my plate. I am looking in horror at the electricity bill. It is for a sum over a thousand pounds. My first thought is that I've accidentally received the bill for the Toledo cinema and my second I lose no time in voicing.

"I've always maintained that there's a dreadful waste of electricity in this house and, from this day on life here is going to change. There's to be no more lights left on in the hall and in rooms that are not occupied. There's to be no more leaving electric blankets on for hours and bedroom heaters are banned from today. I'm removing that fan heater from your room, Scott, and from now on you'll do your schoolwork downstairs at the table in the dining room."

I leave my dinner uneaten and retire to the front room. In my absence Joan and Scott study the bill.

They check the figures on the meter and discover that, in error, the readings have some of the figures in the reverse order. Why didn't I think of checking?

If there's one thing I am quite firm about it is that I don't attempt to do a job that requires the expertise of a tradesman so, when Joan tells me that the fan has slipped on the twin-tub washing machine, I say, "Just ring the chap from Hoover."

Joan protests: "They make a huge call-out charge and I've watched them replace the fan. If you take the back off the washing machine I'll show you what to do but I can't pull the machine away from the wall myself."

I say firmly, "You know my maxim; every man to his own trade. I know nothing about washing machines. Phone the repair man."

I'm a bit rattled when I come home the next day to find the washing machine has, in my absence, been repaired by Joan and Scott. Apparently he could be prevailed upon to supply the co-operation which I was unprepared to give. I wouldn't surprise me if Joan has actually given him half the call-out fee. She is always looking for excuses to add a bonus to his normal pocket money. I wouldn't resent it if he spent it once in a while getting a proper haircut. Like all his generation his hair is straggling below his collar, looking as if it has been handled with a knife and fork rather than a brush and comb. I was earning a living when I was his age while he does little enough to earn his keep. I think left to his own devices he'd lie in bed all day. It takes him all his time to mow the lawn once a week.

1974

Scott did the minimum work for his Highers, but at least he has managed to pass, so he is to be accepted by Strathclyde University at the end of this summer. Why he is choosing to study Psychology, Philosophy, and Sociology along with his maths I have no idea. He says that with the exception of maths he is sick to death of all the subjects he had to study at school. Nothing I say is going to change his mind. It is around this time that Joan tells me Scott has mentioned to her that he and Derek are considering leaving home to share a flat. "What shall we say to dissuade them?" she asks me.

"Nothing at all," I reply. "In fact tell them to go ahead."

"You can't mean that!"

"Indeed I do mean it. Let them consider it for as long as they wish. They might even get around to reckoning how much cash they'll need for the venture. There's the rub. On student grants there's no way either of them can afford to move out. I mean it. Let him know we have no objection and you'll find it never gets mentioned again." It doesn't.

Scott can be very truculent. He is paying for his own driving lessons and always has an excuse for refusing my offers to let him have a go in my car with me beside him. It's a pity because, unlike Joan and Jenny, he is keen to drive and, again unlike them, he is extremely observant. I guess he has taken in quite a lot about driving just from being a passenger. He asks Joan if she is willing to pay for his driving test. Joan says she will pay for the one test that he passes. On the day he sits his first test he is standing at the window to greet her with his thumbs up.

I am pretty confident that Scott will drive carefully. In retrospect it was no bad thing that he and John were both hurt soon after John had passed his driving test a few months ago. I think John was probably speeding which could account for him failing to negotiate a bend and hitting a tree. They both ended up in hospital, John with an injured leg and Scott with several cuts to his face and a broken nose.

So now it's the case that he is always asking if he can borrow the car. At least he pays for his own petrol and is willing to wash the car once in a while and he never takes the car if he is going to have a drink. Joan complains because on Sunday mornings she finds that Scott and his pals have come home late the previous night and drunk all the milk. I tell her that she should be grateful that at his age he mostly drinks milk.

There's no end to Scott's likes and dislikes. It has to be Robertson's Golden Shred marmalade, Heinz Ideal sauce and Robinson's orange squash. Occasionally we go shopping at a hypermarket where, by buying in bulk, we secure much reduced prices. We buy an unknown brand of orange squash. I keep these bottles in the garden hut and refill the Robinson's bottle as necessary. The winter is exceptionally severe, so the squash in the hut freezes, bursts the bottles and we lose it all.

Scott seems much happier in his second year at Strathclyde. At the end of his first year he switched his course to wholly maths. He is working at the cash point in a garage some evenings. During most of the summer vacations he succeeds, more by luck than effort on his part, in acquiring a job of sorts. He has worked in a warehouse storage room, washed buses, and has worked in the local cemetery mowing lawns, more than a bit envious of Steve, who is driving the hearse. When he is not working he signs up for unemployment benefit. I cannot credit that he is actually claiming benefit and I feel certain that this will affect me disadvantageously through my income tax payments.

Scott is up to every dodge in the book. If he and Derek want to go by train into town in the evening they rifle through the bins on the station platform to find discarded tickets that have missed being clipped. I have heard Joan offer him some extra cash when he is about to set out for the students' union on a Saturday night. Scott refuses: "I've got enough money to buy the one drink I intend to buy. If I'm too late to catch the last bus and I have to walk home I don't have anything of value that would make me worth mugging."

"What about your watch?"

"Don't worry. I'd just hand it over."

CHAPTER
TWELVE

1977

This will be the third spring that we are planning to holiday abroad. Our first venture was in the spring of the year that Jenny was married when we flew to Majorca for a week with Dave and Enid. As part of the package we had the use of a Fiat for the holiday. We arrived late on the Saturday. On the Sunday I took a step backwards to allow a couple of guests to enter the hotel lift, tripped and fell down the steps behind me. My leg was in a splint for the next five days so, until our final Friday, my car sat in dock and we took turns to squeeze into the Fiat which Dave was driving.

So the holiday fell short of being a complete success but it was enough to whet our appetites for further holidays abroad. We spent a couple of holidays in Benidorm and another on the Orange Coast of Spain. We both enjoy the sun and sitting outside drinking coffee in the numerous cafés along the sea front. We enjoy browsing round the markets or the shops in the old towns and being entertained by the musical groups who play nightly in the many bars. On one of these holidays we made friends with a London couple, Mary and Les, so we are pleased when they tell us that, with their daughter, they are coming up to Glasgow for the weekend. On the Saturday afternoon of their stay I drive them to Dunoon. I have only had the Fiat a few months. I opted for the smaller car knowing that I will be retiring next year and I want a car I can afford to keep even when I'm a pensioner.

We are booked into a carvery at Charing Cross for a six o'clock meal and we are late starting off on the return journey from Dunoon. I do not like to rush and I am irritated by the delay the others have caused me by their loitering. As it happens we are not held up by traffic so I relax as we reach Glasgow. The carvery is within sight. We have only to negotiate the second of two sets of synchronised traffic lights when a car approaching across our path from the left hits the front passenger seat of the car with a thud. Our three visitors, packed in the back of the Fiat do not suffer much of a shake but Joan's head has bounced against the side window and it is only the bleeding which dulls the excruciating pain in her head.

I cannot believe this has happened. I'm sure the lights were in my favour. Was I slow getting off the mark? Did the driver of the other car jump the lights. I just don't know. It seems the other driver, like myself, is unhurt and, against all the rules we are both in our confusion apologising to one another as we exchange information. Not a cross word is spoken. One of the young policemen who appear on the scene immediately addresses Joan as "Mrs Park" and turns out to be a former pupil of hers. An ambulance is summoned and the other two ladies in the party accompany Joan to the

Royal Infirmary. Meanwhile Les and I, left behind at the scene of the accident, are told by the police that my new car is in no fit state to be driven. They will get it towed to a garage where they will take us so we may clear it of personal belongings and we can get a taxi home.

In the house we wait for hours wondering what kind of injuries Joan has that require the others to be so long at the hospital. At last a taxi brings them to the door and Joan comes in with her head swathed in bandages. I feel so guilt-ridden. I set the table and got a meal on the way hours ago but I can hardly manage a mouthful. Apparently Joan could not stop shivering at the hospital so she was put in a wheelchair, wrapped in blankets and taken to a cubicle where she waited to get her head examined, just one of the many casualties, much more serious than hers, which have to be treated in a Glasgow hospital on a normal Saturday night. Some hours later the cut in her head was stitched and, after yet another long wait, she was allowed to leave. She says she cannot think why they felt it necessary to bandage her head. Because our friends' weekend has been ruined, we salvage the Sunday by taking taxis back to the carvery for lunch. I find it difficult to be good company but at least I insist on picking up the bills.

I am dreading the impending court case, which the police tell me may not happen until a year from now. How will I be able to tell the truth about how the accident was caused when it was a blur at the time and I fail to see how that can become any clearer? Whether or not it was my fault I feel I am the one to blame.

On the Monday, our friends having left by train Joan goes to school and I go into the office. When I arrive at work I cannot stop the tremors which shake me, so my office colleagues insist that I return home. Joan seems to have completely recovered but when she comes in at four and hears my story she calls the doctor. He puts me on tranquillizers and for the weeks which follow I feel like a zombie. Joan seeks out the doctor and tells him that she thinks the tablets are too strong. The doctor changes the tablets but I sleep in the chair for most of the day. I wake from time to time but on rising I stumble and fail to keep my balance. I must look as if I am drunk. I am haunted by the thought of the court case, worried that I will be unable to recall the details.

One good thing which emerges is that because the wrecked car is less than a year old we are refunded in full by insurance and, with the help of Scott for both the purchase and the collection, we have its twin sitting in the garage. I am determined to get driving again but watching me staggering to get myself into the driving seat fills both Joan and Scott with horror. One day Joan actually hides my car keys. She insists that I am a danger even to myself to be driving a car. This remark does little to assuage my bruised self-esteem.

Scott is better at dealing with me as I am at present. He cracks jokes and makes light of my shortcomings. He is in his final year at Strathclyde. He spent the summer working for the civil service in London. He worked in an office at statistics and tells us they have a pretty haphazard way of arriving at figures. The end of Scott's third year saw him still with some re-sits so what is going to happen this year is in the lap of the gods. I don't think it is possible to re-sit final exams so it's my guess that when he has no option Scott will do enough work to get through. He must be hopeful of passing for at least he is sending off applications for jobs. He wants to get taken on by a computer firm. There's more than a bit of confusion when Joan answers a phone call requesting a Mr Park, directs them to me at the office only for me to discover that the conversation making no sense to me is intended for Scott.

These firms all seem to be based in London and they stump up for to Scott to fly down for interviews. To tell you the truth I won't be sorry when he moves out. His room badly needs decorating. I've no idea when I'm going to manage to get into it. I tell Scott: "I want the room cleared of all your stuff when you move out. Anything that you are not taking with you can be housed in the garage. I'd guess most of it is only fit for the bin."

As I predicted Scott is successful in achieving his degree. In March 1978 he is planning his 21st birthday party. Joan supplies some of the food and his girlfriend helps him collect the rest and transport it to the selected venue. During the Easter holiday Joan and I take a luxury holiday in Tenerife to celebrate our silver wedding. Some friends and family insist on some present money for the occasion, so we treat ourselves to a new TV set which makes it possible for us to view in colour.

In October 1978 we attend Scott's graduation ceremony and finally the day arrives for Scott to pack up and go down to live in London. We discover that the head of the firm he is going to work for is someone who has been a friend of Joan's since they were children. When Joan tells Scott he is not too happy. He is hoping that he is being taken on because of his own qualifications and handling of the interview. He certainly doesn't want to have succeeded because his mother was known to the boss. Joan rings her friend to tell him what has happened. He thinks it all a great joke. "Tell Scott he need have no worries. I'm chiefly in the main Liverpool office. London is just one of several offshoots. It is only very seldom that I visit them. Each office is managed independently and hire and fire their own staff." Scott is reassured and is looking forward to sharing a flat with Derek and a third lad. They hire a car to get most of their belongings down to London and finally we see Scott off on the train.

I am driving home and it is less than an hour since we saw Scott leave when I find myself saying, "I didn't realise how different it would be without Scott. I'll fairly miss him."

Joan smiles, "Alex, a week ago you were still badgering him for his leaving date. You were the same when Jenny moved out. Is it men in general or is it just you that refuses to use your imagination to see beyond the present?"

I make no reply but I ponder her words as I try to busy myself getting down to re-decorating Scott's room.

As October 1978 arrives it is my 65th birthday and I have to admit I do not welcome retirement. I seem to have no zest for anything these days. How am I going to pass my days without going to the office? I say to Joan, "You are still working three days a week. I don't relish putting in half of every week on my own. I'm not asking you to give up. I know you enjoy it and the extra cash will come in handy when I only have the state pension but I'm not expecting it to be easy for me to adjust to the change." My bosses ask me to carry on part time in a consultant capacity which I am more then happy to accept.

The family all give me presents which they think will add to my enjoyment of my new-found leisure hours. Joan gives me an expensive Reader's Digest DIY book and a tool called a Jigsaw. I'm really not planning to turn myself into a carpenter so they are both safely put away for the time being. Jenny and Martin give me a barbecue. It won't be getting used until next summer and only then if the Scottish summer surprises us with weather that is better than our norm. It goes in the loft. In fact it never does see the light of day again and some years later Jenny suggests that as it has never been used perhaps she could have it back. Scott presents me with a useful car accessory which he knows I will appreciate.

There are many other gifts from the staff I have worked with over the years. A group of clerkesses subscribe to present me with a crystal fruit bowl. I receive a really beautiful Bible from Maisie, the chief clerkess with whom I have always enjoyed an excellent working relationship. Asked to suggest an idea for a presentation gift I had mentioned a Teasmade so I am pleased to pass this on as a present to Joan. She protests, "You don't like drinking tea in bed and it's your retirement, not mine."

"I'm aware of that but in that I bring you up a cup of tea every morning to help you waken up while I'm in the bathroom, now as the alarm goes off you can pour your own tea and it will save me a trip upstairs."

Everyone at Simpson and Shaw knows that I am a "home and family" man. I don't want a send-off party with loads of drink. There are a few speeches and a few handshakes and it is all over. After all I'll be back in the office after I return from what can now become a regular autumn holiday in Spain. I'm hoping that this holiday makes up for the rotten summer holiday we had this year. We had a self-catering flat in Buxton. As it turned out the walls which separated the various flatlets were paper-thin and although there was a garden the weather was so poor that we were never sitting in it. It was not a relaxing holiday at all. We seemed to be driving round in the rain most of the time. When we did stop somewhere there was little to tempt me to leave the car.

Thelma was with us so she and Joan would wander round while I sat in the car with my paper. I was usually glad to get back to the flat and that wasn't so easy as the traffic built up in the late afternoon. Since the accident I seem to have lost a bit of confidence. On one occasion Joan accused me of going through a red light. I don't know what happened that made her suppose I could possibly behave so badly on the road.

Now that there are only the two of us, Joan and I can make the trip to Liverpool more often. The drive tires me out a bit but we are always made so welcome. Joan's Mum thinks that under the pretext of watching some golf or snooker with her I deserve to have a nap in the chair and we are fed like kings. Joan's mother can no longer see the television too clearly. On her own she listens to radio and to "talking books". She suffers from macular degeneration and is now registered blind. She cannot read a newspaper but she receives a regular radio cassette with both local and national news. She asks my opinion on current events and I find she is far better informed than I am. In one of these conversations I talk about playing Patience and watching some rubbish on the television. My final comment is, "It passes the time."

Joan's mother gives me a long look over the top of her glasses repeating, "Passing the time! Is that what you said, 'passing the time'? Well, you are in your sixties and I am nearly twenty years older than you, but thank God I haven't yet reached the stage of trying to PASS the time."

The clergyman who married us usually comes to the Lowes' house to see us if he knows we are visiting. He realises I am far from well and is very sympathetic. As he is about to leave Joan is in the hall with him. I overhear some of the conversation. "It's hardly surprising, Joan. All in the same year he has become semi-retired, lost the companionship of Scott and had a car accident. Any one of these could have triggered his depression. You take care of him."

"I know. I do try. I'm also trying to survive, myself."

"Oh, indeed yes. It can't be easy for you."

124

I still have not recovered when we decide to visit Jenny and Martin. Jenny attained her doctorate and is now lecturing. They have moved to London. We are travelling by train on the Tuesday after the Easter bank holiday. Even as we board the train at Glasgow Central it is obvious that the seating accommodation has been overbooked. The authorities apparently do not intend to put on an extra coach. With our luggage I stand between two compartments while Joan goes the length of the train looking for two unoccupied seats. She finds plenty in first class and in third class there is a whole empty coach reserved for Saga passengers.

Against my better judgement she persuades me to sit in the Saga coach. Her argument is that the group may be joining the train further south so meantime we may well occupy the seats. A troubled father, unable to find a seat for his teenage daughter travelling alone, asks if he may leave her on the third seat beside us.

Minutes before we are due to leave the Saga party arrives. I rise prepared to move but Joan restrains me. "Nobody is going to suspect that we are not with Saga. We are in the same age group." It soon becomes evident that three Saga passengers are left without seats.

I say, "We can't stay here. We have to give up these seats."

"Hang on," Joan insists. "There's no way you can stand all the way to London. You'll see, the guard will be summoned and these people will be able to demand that they be seated in first class. We can't demand that. They won't have to stand as we would."

It happens as she predicts and, for a while all is well. About one station down the line the ticket inspector reaches our coach. The Saga group are displaying their tickets in their special issue folders. To maintain the bluff Joan clutches the folder that holds our "two for the price of one" tickets which we obtained through a sales promotion from Persil washing powder. The ticket inspector is making his way along our side of the compartment. When he reaches us in the last three seats, it is obvious that the young person sitting next to us cannot possibly be travelling with Saga. We explain how she was put in the seat by her father. The ticket collector apologises but insists on her vacating the seat and accompanies her to join the other standing passengers in the space between the carriages. He returns some minutes later and resumes his ticket inspection down the other side of the coach. Happily for us we are never asked to produce our tickets.

I'm truly puzzled by the incongruities in Joan's conduct which I am continually discovering. While seemingly incapable of telling a direct lie, she has no qualms about assuming a totally dishonest stance if it is to her advantage. Perhaps I misjudge her. On this occasion I know she would have stood all the way to London so I suppose she carried out the fraud for my benefit. She looks on it all as a bit of a joke but it makes me very uncomfortable. I'll make sure we are the first in the queue for the return journey. I'm not having a repeat of this fiasco.

CHAPTER
THIRTEEN

Some time in the early eighties I decided that I no longer wished to continue going into the office in my part-time capacity which made me feel neither fish nor fowl. The dreaded court case never happened. It was a long time before I found out that the two insurance firms settled on a knock for knock basis and only then was the load lifted from my mind. I had been taking sleeping pills ever since the car accident and I knew that I had to work at getting myself off them. I changed my car and, because the new one was unfamiliar to me, I drove out daily to get myself accustomed to the model and at the same time I gradually cut out the sleeping pills. I don't lack willpower and I had determined to succeed. I think it was mastering these two challenges which gradually restored my self-confidence.

After the disastrous holiday in Buxton we spend some great holidays once again in the sunny south. We find some excellent self-catering accommodation in the Cotswolds until these prices rise so high that we switch to a cottage in Yorkshire. Jenny and Martin join us for two or three days on a couple of these holidays. Jenny is no longer lecturing because in 1980 I became a grandfather to their new baby, Kim. Jenny always said she wanted a family rather than a career. She wanted to be an educated Mum. On getting his second degree Martin took up social work so they live on a shoestring. They both look like a couple of tramps and Jenny buys clothes for her toddler in charity shops. It all seems a bit of a waste of talent to me. We drove down to London for the christening and I had to make a speech. I say christening but it was just a non-christening party. I find it difficult to be thrilled at becoming a granddad when the opportunities are few and far between to see my grandchild.

Martin has since gained a promoted post in the Midlands, so we see the house they are hoping to buy in a lovely little village which will be far better for them than the districts they have lived in since they married.

Joan goes down to see them as often as she can when she gets a school holiday. I do not choose to accompany her. It's a long drive and I have to admit I cannot adapt to their late evening meals. Also, it seems to me that they give in to Kim far too much. She seems to get her own way over everything. I suppose her wilfulness stems from her mother except I made sure that Jenny did as she was told.

1982
It is the year of the football world cup. In July of this year a rail strike is threatened. As school breaks up at the end of June, Joan is planning to spend a few days with Jenny. I reason with her: "Suppose you get there

and you can't get home again. What about our own Yorkshire cottage booked later in the month?"

"The strike may never happen. Anyway, if I can't get home by train I'll find some way of getting myself to Skipton or you could pick me up at Leicester. I've left some extra holiday clothes packed which you can put in the car for me. I'll have other things I need at Jenny's. Oh, and there's a box of groceries packed so we have what we need to see us through the first couple of days at the cottage."

"I'll never understand you, Joan. Don't you ever worry?"

"You do enough worrying for the two of us. What kind of life would we have if we both worried? And to answer your question, I'm certainly not going to waste my energy being concerned about something which may never happen."

Joan goes into town. To make enquiries in case she cannot travel by train, she stands in a long queue at the bus station and it is there that her wallet is stolen from the pocket of her shopping bag. She loses over a hundred pounds. She is very careless with money. Once she lost the whole of her salary because after a day at school she went directly from the bank to an evening class. Fortunately for her, some honest person handed it in. On another occasion she laid her purse down on a shop counter and once again was able to retrieve it. This time she is not so lucky. The police return the wallet months later. It was found empty behind a shelf when a betting shop was being redecorated. Joan says,

"I wonder if the bet he made with my money resulted in a win."

As it happens she is able to leave by train. Within two days the rail strike begins. It is the day after the outbreak of the strike when I am looking forward to spending the afternoon in front of the television, watching an important football match. I've made myself fish and chips and, so as not to miss the start of the game I carry my meal through to the sitting room where I become engrossed in the action. I'm aware of nothing until I hear a shattering of glass. It sounds like the kitchen windows.

I open the door of the sitting room and I am met with clouds of smoke. As I reach the dining room the flames are licking across the ceiling tiles which are liquefying and dropping on the carpet. I think it is at that point that I dial 999 for the fire brigade. The glass door between the dining room and the kitchen is in pieces and the kitchen curtains are ablaze. I grab the smoking chip pan and throw it out of the kitchen door. I grab towels to try to beat out the flames. I remember the small fire extinguisher on the wall but it is useless against this inferno. My next door neighbour is yelling at me to get out but I'm still trying to fight the fire when the fire engine arrives and the firemen take over with hoses.

I suppose it is shock but I'm not conscious of any pain until in the ambulance that is taking me to hospital I realise that my hands and face are burnt and even my eyebrows are singed. The police come to the hospital to tell me that for security they have boarded up the back of the house after the firemen left. They tell me that the Wardens, our neighbours on the opposite side of the avenue, will be coming to collect me when the burns have been treated and dressed. I am to sleep in their house. The police have also rung Joan to tell her what has happened. It is when I am in the Wardens' house that I get the phone call from Joan.

"I'm just waiting until Martin gets in from work. He is going to drive me home this evening. It's a new car and he is still running it in so we won't be in Glasgow until the early hours of the morning."

"Joan, there's nowhere for you to sleep. The whole house is filled with smoke and soot. There's no kitchen left. They've cut off the electricity and there's no power so there's no lights. I don't know whether we can live in the house any more. It's all my fault. I'm so sorry." I break down.

"The house doesn't matter, Alex. You're still alive. When I got the telephone call from the police my first thought was you had been in a car accident. I'll see you in the morning."

Joan and Martin look very grubby when they appear at Wardens' next morning. They did the rounds of the house by torchlight and in that dim light thought the beds looked so inviting that there was no necessity to use the sleeping bags they had brought with them. They collapsed on to the top of the beds only to find when they awoke that they were covered in soot. At the Wardens' they wash and we all eat breakfast before Martin starts back on the return journey. I try to thank Martin by offering him the petrol money for his journey but he refuses, laughing and saying that now he has covered the required mileage he'll be able to make better speed back home. I think he is aware that I can't thank him enough for getting Joan here.

Jenny has rung Scott and he is with us by two o'clock. Through the boarding we can see that the kitchen is a roofless shell. The few kitchen utensils which have survived are strewn round the garden as are the burnt-out cooker and washing machine. Even the lino on the floor has melted and the timber is charred. Our neighbours have rallied and are housing the food which has been removed from our fridge and freezer and for the rest of the week they hand in meals. Someone even gives us a cooking stove. In the blackened dining room the contents of the sideboard cupboards provide us with dishes and Joan finds the box of food she had left ready for us to take on holiday. That is a holiday which has to be cancelled. This means that Joan's sister Thelma will also get no holiday. Maybe she can come and stay with us later on this summer.

I have to attend outpatients every second day to get the burns redressed. My hands and face and head are bandaged. I don't seem to be in any pain but I can't hold a knife and fork or even a spoon and there's nothing I can do to help Scott and Joan with all the cleaning. Scott shops for us and brings in loads of cleaning materials. He also takes an inventory of all the destroyed items in the garden and helps Joan to recall the kitchen contents which are no longer there. He takes her to Pearson's store on Victoria Road to price the replacements which will have to be claimed from the insurance.

The electrician arrives to make everything safe and reconnect us. I'm taking this opportunity to get the whole house rewired. Once we have hot water Joan strips down all the sooted bedlinen, curtains and covers. She washes them in the bath and uses the old baby bath to carry them out of the front door and round to the clothesline in the back garden. There they drip in the sun until they are dry. She never stops working, washing down doors and door handles and even the laminated walls of the dining room. As soon as she has finished one chore the soot in the air re-settles and she has to start all over again. My bandages become grey in a matter of hours.

The insurance assessor is very kind and very sympathetic but he has to inform us that we are under-insured and that all large items such as the fridge, cooker and washing machine are worth very little because electrical goods devalue. Ours are over ten years old and the "new for old" clause did not exist when we took out the policy. He suggests that at their expense we move into a hotel but I cannot face that. He says, "Well, at least get a decorator in to clear the debris from the dining room and wash the walls." To Joan he adds, "You must obtain two estimates from which I will make the choice for the necessary repairs."

Joan contacts two building firms, who view the damage. The first wish to rebuild the kitchen with the custom-built wall unit which we had originally. The second is obviously prepared to do more of a patch-up job. It is Scott who insists that they speak in a layman's language that he can understand. When the estimates come in they are poles apart. Joan tries to convince the assessor that she should secure a third estimate but he assures her he will be able to choose between the two. By the time he agrees that this is impossible, it is the middle of July. It is the Glasgow Fair holiday and all the building firms have closed down for a fortnight. As she rings one firm after another, all Joan gets is answering machines. Finally the assessor helps us by suggesting a small builder who specialises in extensions who he is sure he can trust to give us a good job. This builder is happy to take on the work but will be unable to start until the middle of August as his men take their holidays in the first fortnight of that month.

By this time Scott has had to return to London so Neil comes to drive me to and fro the hospital. He often stays on for an hour or two to keep me company knowing how little time Joan has to spare. Because we have no fridge she has to shop more often and the chores of washing and cooking take twice as long as they normally would. I feel very low. I seem to have just recovered from years of depression only to be flung back into the same state.

The day the builders are due to start work is the same day that Joan's school term begins. I just cannot face trying to answer the numerous questions which could arise in Joan's absence. I am unsure what she has settled for by way of a compromise and even if she tells me I don't think I could take it in. The very thought of the house invaded by workmen fills me with horror.

134

Joan knows how I feel and makes an arrangement with her headmaster whereby she will go into school whenever she is able.

We open our doors to a joiner, a plasterer, a brickie, a plumber, and an electrician who have the use of the dining room as the kitchen gives no shelter from the elements. They use our electric kettle to brew up as soon as they arrive and frequently through the day they are enjoying their tea-breaks. Joan mentions this to their boss who laughs and says that no manual worker can keep on the job all through the day. We mustn't worry. He trusts his men and the job will get done on time.

At last comes the day when the assessor arrives to settle our claim. He tells us that because we have been so undemanding it is only fair that the insurance company should be generous. They are allowing us the full value of the main kitchen items, namely the cooker, washing machine and fridge. New wall units, curtains, linoleum, china, food stuffs, radio cassette and all the other items we listed as lost in the fire are covered by the cheque we receive. The tradesmen's bills which they have accepted include those of the glazier, the carpet and upholstery cleaners, and the bill from the decorator allows for the repainting of the whole house. The assessor stresses that we are in no way responsible for any extra expenses over and above the claims put in by the tradesmen.

It is fortunate for us that we are forewarned. The glazier complains that the glass he is replacing in the doors is costing more than he estimated because regulations on the weight of the glass he must use have been changed. The joiner and the electrician each refuse to stand the cost of replacing a new cable accidentally severed. Joan constantly refuses their demands with the words of the assessor. She adds, "If you have a good case you contact the assessor and see if he will come up with the extra payment".

We are told that it is now impossible to obtain a match for the section of dining room laminate that was destroyed. The decorator helps us out. He suggest that we fill the space with some built-in shelving but cautions us that when the matter is discussed with the builder, we have to let him think it is his idea. This, of course, is the kind of dissembling which comes second nature to my wife. For my part I'd rather pay out to get it done.

It is October when the last tradesman leaves. Thelma comes up to stay with us and we have a spending spree to buy all the bits and pieces which were lost. I find it all very tiring.

CHAPTER
FOURTEEN

1984

Joan is working through her last year as a remedial teacher and she will stop at the end of June. I won't be sorry. Joan brings up my breakfast on the three days each week before she goes to school and I usually collect her at four o'clock but it is a long day for me to put in on my own.

Once Joan is at home full time we enjoy our days. I make the coffee and toast and we sit over a leisurely breakfast doing the Target puzzle in the daily newspaper. I can drive us to the local supermarket or further afield to the East Kilbride shopping centre. We regularly have a weekly pub lunch somewhere and an occasional trip to Ayr. The garden keeps me busy and I enjoy watching sport on television.

Joan is always doing something. We now have three grandchildren for whom Joan is always sewing some outfit or another. I ask her why she wants to spend her time doing this when we could buy them. She says she enjoys doing the things she never had time to do when she was teaching. With the cash she received from colleagues as a retirement present she has bought a loom and taken up weaving. She buys fleece, cards it and spins it on a hand-held wooden spindle. Recently she has joined a craft club where she makes cards, pictures and cushions in needlepoint. She also makes quilled designs and has started to take a stall at craft fairs.

When we are on holiday she'll spend ages in a toy shop or craft shop where, inspired by some of their expensive products, none of which she buys, she will later supply herself with the linen or the felt or the clay to reproduce replicas of them. Such items are "play pictures" where, say, the clothes on the clothes line are removable, or the miniature "play food", made from clay and painted to make fruit and bread and plates of sausage and chips, with which to stock the toy shop or restaurant that she is making for the grandchildren.

I look forward to the holidays in sunny Spain, which we usually take in October, and less so to those we take in Yorkshire in June or July. We combine these holidays with a visit to Joan's mum in Liverpool and, because Thelma is looking after their mum, we give her a break by taking her with us on holiday. Some years Mrs. Lowe comes and stays with us for a few weeks from the end of May but since she has lost her sight she comes less regularly.

We go down to Liverpool more often now that we are no longer working. I find it tiring driving on the motorway. We try to arrange to travel on a Sunday when there's less traffic. Even so I am relieved when we get there and I can put my feet up, watch some golf on television and maybe have a bit of shut-eye. Thelma has always excelled herself at the roast dinner and a variety of baking, and Joan's mum makes us very welcome. She invites former friends to visit during our stay and we lunch out with others or accompany them for days out in Southport or Chester.

We take Joan's mum with us to Widnes where she enjoys sitting in a hotel with a whisky while we look for bargains in the market before joining her for coffee. On our way there or back we visit Millie, my hostess back in March '53 who, after one or two strokes, is often at a loss for the right word. As a substitute she constantly uses the word "tomato" and for the same reason refers to me as "Nancy". She has not lost her baking skills nor her memory for recipes, so we feast on home-made sausage rolls and eccles cakes.

One such day we take Millie and her friend out to lunch. Because we cannot all fit into my car together, I make two trips. On the second trip I leave the car unattended to give some assistance to the older ladies climbing the steps into the hotel. I intend coming back to get it parked properly. The engine is still running when Thelma behind me steps out of the car and closes all the doors. My car keys are inside and I've no way of getting into the car.

I have to take a taxi back to the Lowes' home to pick up my spare keys. When the taxi brings me back it is to find that several well-wishers have been experimenting with their own car keys and my lock is damaged. I am so angry with Thelma that it takes me all my time to be civil. How could anybody be so stupid? I flatter myself that I do not openly lose my temper but this kind of control takes a lot out of me and that night I discover that a couple of my fingers refuse to function properly and they never do recover.

One way or another Thelma is the cause of much irritation to me. She will never willingly admit her ignorance on any subject, even when proved wrong. She frequently gives me incorrect directions when I am driving on Merseyside (I've unintentionally ended up in a car park before now) and she assumes an air of authority on every topic. Her favourite statement is, "I know". She and I often fall out while Joan is the pig-in-the-middle trying to keep the peace.

Joan is in the same position when Jenny and her family stay with us. I've never really felt comfortable with Martin. I always have the impression that he is classifying me according to the criteria he uses in his professional capacity. As for Jenny's children, both she and Martin have made a rod for their own back there. Sometimes Joan goes down to collect the children as their schools break up for the summer holiday. She'll take them to Liverpool for the first half of the week and possibly leave one with Thelma while she brings the other two up here. I have to say that during the week here they behave quite reasonably and we don't have any nonsense when it comes to their bedtime. Within five minutes of their parents' return, there's trouble and for the rest of the time they are with us they demand so much attention that I'm relieved when the house becomes our own again.

Joan accepts the fact that I prefer to stay at home on the couple of times each year that she takes herself down to Jenny's. I usually make the excuse that I'm going to welcome the chance to get on with some decorating. On one of these occasions I take a dizzy turn when I'm up the ladder. Scott phones me, as he does daily if Joan is away, and I tell him I feel less than well so he rings Jenny. He tells me he asked Martin to pass this news on to Joan, but Joan does not return any sooner than she had intended.

It is for quite another reason that about a year later I end up in hospital. I am waiting to have an operation for a bit of prostate trouble. I spend two or three days under observation and then I am told they are not operating after all and I can go home. I ring to tell Joan to bring my clothes in. Because she wasn't expecting this news she has arranged for upholstery cleaners to call but she arranges for me to be collected by a neighbour.

I am waiting for him to arrive when a doctor stops at my bed and in two short sentences informs me that I have cancer of the prostate gland and will receive the necessary medication to check its growth. There are no screens round the bed. There is no counselling of any kind. I am completely shattered.

When I confide in Joan, she fails to see how serious it is. She says, "Prostate cancer in men is quite common. It doesn't mean you are going to die of it."

I can only think of an article I read recently — someone in the French government who had died five years after the onset of prostate cancer. "Suppose I have to get radiotherapy or chemotherapy, how will I cope with that?"

"But nobody's suggested that and you can always say 'No' It's your choice."

In the following weeks and months nobody does suggest that. I take the four daily tablets and life goes on pretty much the same as usual.

1987

It is a spring morning and I am working in the garden when Joan tells me she has to go to the supermarket. I'm in my working clothes but I offer to run her down in the car. With a trolley full of shopping we reach the check-out and it is only then that Joan discovers she hasn't enough cash to cover the bill.

"What money have you got?" she asks me.

"I didn't bring any cash. These are my working clothes."

"Never mind," is her reply. "We'll have to go to the bank."

She then asks the assistant if we can leave the shopping to collect when we return with the payment. Joan appears to be not in the least put out. I am thoroughly embarrassed and her total lack of concern makes me very angry. As always, I am determined not to give vent to my rage so I bury it and seethe inwardly. We complete the expedition in silence and on our return home I get back to my digging which helps somewhat to ease my bad feelings.

I come in from the garden to find Joan has tried to make amends by cooking my favourite lunch. I'm hungry after my efforts and I tuck into the steak pie and the fruit tart. Joan spends the early part of the afternoon washing dishes and generally cleaning up the kitchen while I go through to watch the Snooker. I am suffering some acute indigestion and more than once I go through to the kitchen to get a soft drink to ease it. It is about four o'clock when, as Joan is pouring me another drink, she asks, "Where are you getting the pain?" I tell her it's lying right across my chest.

"In the tops of your arms, as well?"

"Yes."

"I'll ring the doctor."

"That's not necessary."

She rings the surgery to say she thinks I am suffering a heart attack. The doctor's answer is: "Don't wait for me to come. Ring for an ambulance or, better still, if there's a neighbour who can drive you to the hospital, just go there yourselves."

I'm in hospital for a week while they do all the tests which prove I have had a heart attack. My mother and two brothers died of heart attacks so I'm worried. Joan says, "If you only take your first heart attack halfway through your seventies, there's not too much wrong with your lifestyle. We'll cut down on fatty foods, buy semi-skimmed milk and use margarine instead of butter." I have been told to take a daily walk and not to drive for several months.

Joan's mother will be celebrating her 90th birthday at the end of May. She is planning a celebration lunch to which family and a few friends are invited. About two weeks before the planned occasion we receive the sad news that she has died that morning. We empty the fridge and take the food with us to Liverpool as Scott has driven up from London to drive us there. A week later Scott drives us back home. He stays with us overnight and, the next morning offers to take Joan shopping to replenish the fridge before his drive home. Joan says, "No. You get away early. Neil said I could ring him if I ever needed transport." She arranges for Neil to meet her in the supermarket.

She sets off down the road as I leave the house to do my usual walk in the opposite direction. She trips on an uneven flagstone and shatters her right wrist. She carries on to the supermarket and asks Neil to run her to the hospital. Just by chance they spot me on the main road so I join them. While Joan's wrist is being x-rayed and put in plaster, Neil and I pick up the shopping she was unable to buy. For the next few weeks I am required to do the jobs which Joan is unable to cope with. My own convalescence is cut short.

In August Jenny and her family are with us for their usual summer holiday. Most days Joan is attending the hospital for wax treatment on the wrist. We have our breakfast with any of Jenny's family who are out of bed in time to join us, and the rest are just appearing when Joan and I are leaving for the hospital. I drop Joan off and, knowing that the breakfast and clearing up will still be going on, I drive into a car park and enjoy a bit of peace with my newspaper. It is months later that I discover that, after the hospital treatment, Joan, for similar reasons, spent half an hour in the nearby café before she took the bus home.

CHAPTER
FIFTEEN

It is a July summer morning and, as we get home from church the sun is shining and I set the deckchairs out in the garden before coming in for my lunch. The clouds appear so we settle inside with a TV *Columbo*. As the rain begins to fall I leave Joan watching the programme and dash outside to retrieve the deck chairs. I put them in the garage and open the kitchen door. The next thing I know Joan is standing beside me while I sit with my head in my hands and the blood pours out of ears and mouth. When the ambulance arrives, Joan tells the ambulance men that she thinks I may have knocked my head on the garage door or fallen on the kitchen floor.

I spend the rest of the day on a stretcher in Emergency at the Victoria Infirmary. There's a nurse who keeps monitoring my pulse. She is puzzled because it is so low. In the early evening I am admitted to a ward. One minute I am conscious, the next I am not. Doctors come and go. Anne, our next door neighbour, arrives with my pyjamas and some money for Joan, who had not thought to bring her purse. A consultant appears at about nine o'clock. He tells Joan that I am to be transferred to the Southern General to be given a brain scan but, it being a Sunday, an ambulance may not be available until after midnight.

A nurse accompanies us in the ambulance. At the Southern General Joan waits while I am taken for the brain scan and admitted to a ward. Anne brings Joan in to see me the next morning and I am still vomiting blood. Joan listens to the consultant who did the brain scan saying there is a haematoma, evidence of a fall but not a recent one. Perhaps it was when Joan was away and I fell off the ladder. One of the times I wake up Jenny and Scott are at the bedside and Jenny tells the ward sister that, despite the constant bleeding, I'm to be allowed to wear my pyjama jacket.

At the end of a week I am sent back to an orthopaedic ward in the Victoria Infirmary. I cannot see properly and I have difficulty in hearing what Joan is saying. The ward is full of young men, mostly injured in motorcycle accidents, who recover quickly and go home. I don't know why they keep me here. I would be better at home. The ward sister complains to Joan that I am a difficult patient, making no progress at getting myself to the bathroom and leaving most of the meals untouched. Joan points out that I need assistance because I cannot see properly.

Eye and ear tests are set up. Joan accompanies me to the eye-test thinking I will be unable to hear the questions that are put to me. In the small room where this takes place I can hear perfectly. Apparently it is just such a noisy ward at visiting times that I fail to make sense of conversation that is directed at me. The eye-tests prove that I am suffering from double vision, which they seem to think could clear with time.

Scott has driven up from London to keep an appointment with my consultant. He and Joan attend this together. As a result, just in my dressing gown and slippers, I am driven home in Scott's car. When we reach home I cannot get up the stairs unaided. The subsequent months are filled with outpatient appointments and with nurses attending us at home to deal with bedsores and with teaching me how to use a zimmer frame. Despite an operation I am still left with the double vision. Joan borrows large print books and taped book cassettes from the library but I find it difficult to concentrate. I prefer to watch television programmes of sport or films. I enjoy the old films because I remember the plots and if I fall asleep in the middle of them I can pick up the story when I wake up.

Joan tells me she has cancelled both the Yorkshire holiday and the two weeks we had booked in Benidorm. I can't believe she did this without any discussion with me. I am very disappointed. I was so looking forward to some sunshine.

Friends take us to and fro on the outpatient visits, which exhaust me. Scott pays a large deposit into an account with a local taxi firm. He has instructed them to inform him when it needs topping up. I cannot summon much enthusiasm for Christmas when it comes this year. Scott comes up with his girlfriend Eleanor, and Thelma comes as usual. Joan shops for all the presents and puts her usual amount of zeal into all the preparations. I'm glad that for her sake there's some family here to make her effort worthwhile. I am poor company these days.

She does all the shopping on her own as the car lies idle in the garage. There are always prescriptions of one kind or another to be collected for me and I am so weak she is helping me to wash and making meals to tempt my poor appetite. I've given up trying to walk round the block with a zimmer frame. I know I don't use it as the therapist taught me, but I'm too old a dog to learn new tricks. It might be easier if we didn't live on a hill, and icy surfaces don't help. Because I get so little exercise other health problems arise and I'm always falling even in the house.

It is a very poor spring this year and it is far from warm enough to sit in the garden. Joan has had to take over the garden. I watch her from the window and she isn't nearly as methodical as I would be. I don't think she knows the difference between a weed and a flower. She has been dealing with the bills for some time now. It all happened when I saw from the bank statement that an extra charge of forty pounds had been made. When Joan examined the statement, she said it was because our account had gone into the red. In no uncertain terms I told her that could not be the reason. Never, ever in my life had I let an account go into the red. Regardless of my protestations she went to see the bank manager and succeeded in getting a refund of the charge on condition that she took over the dealings with our joint account.

I'm not pleased: "If you think you can do better then you are welcome to try. You've certainly changed. It's not so long ago that you expected me to write your bank cheques, on the excuse that you did it so seldom you couldn't remember the procedure."

Another of her recent actions which shocked me was that, on the suggestion from our social worker neighbour, she put in an application for me to claim attendance allowance.

"How much is that?" I ask.

"About thirty pounds a week, I think."

"We don't need it."

"We do, Alex. I'm having to pay out for all kinds of extra items from the chemist and we are not going to continue letting Scott pay into the taxi account."

"If you get it you can keep it. You can call it your money. I'll have nothing to do with it."

One day our new, brash young doctor drops in to see me. It's the first time for months that I've seen any doctor from our practice. Among the questions he asks me is am I capable of making a meal for myself. It is a ridiculous question. Joan makes the meals. I say, "I suppose I could. Yes." When Joan returns with her shopping, I tell her about the doctor's visit and my answers to his questions.

"Tell me, Alex," she asks, "how do you fill a kettle at the sink with your stick in one hand and balancing yourself by clutching on to the sink top with the other?"

"That's of no consequence. The occasion is never going to arise is it?" Joan shakes her head in despair.

She'll be telling me next that she has managed to attach an electric plug. Up to the present she has resisted all my attempts to teach her this simple

149

operation, but nothing would surprise me about what she is at present willing to try when she makes up her mind to it. It was her determination which brought about an incident which I would prefer to forget.

Joan hasn't a very high opinion of the young doctors who have taken over the practice since my illness began. When I was becoming in every way less able, she spent weeks trying to secure an appointment to see the doctor to find out the reason for this. She was determined to ask him to arrange for me to visit the consultant who did the brain scan. Out of the blue the doctor appeared one Saturday lunchtime and within minutes was prepared to leave, having left a prescription for tablets to alleviate depression.

Joan said, "Is it depression that is making it impossible to walk up the stairs without help? We have to find out why he has got steadily worse over the last six months. I want a second opinion from a consultant."

"Completely unnecessary. The chemist closes at one o'clock. You get down there and put in the prescription."

"Is that a refusal?"

I don't want to hear the argument that follows. I sit with my head in my hands, while the doctor loses his temper, hammers on the table to stress his opinions and tears up the prescription which he flings in Joan's face. Joan stayed calm but my guess is that inwardly she was seething with rage. Through sheer doggedness and not without a couple of threats she succeeded in getting

150

what she wanted. He agreed to contact the Southern General and make the necessary appointment.

Friends take us to the hospital, where I have to proceed in a wheelchair. The consultant talks for a long time and I get tired of listening. He talks about a series of mini-strokes too small to show up in any scan but each leaving behind some diminishment of mental and bodily functions. He concludes by saying. "Your G.P. can only try to prevent further strokes with the aspirin he has prescribed. Other than that he just has to treat the conditions the strokes have left in their wake."

When we come away I say to Joan, "He's saying he doesn't know, isn't he?"

"No, Alex. He's saying that because you are approaching eighty we have to accept that you may have suffered a series of mini-strokes."

"That's what I thought. He's saying he doesn't know."

I get more depressed as the days go by and I get worse instead of better. I can't see us getting away on holiday in the near future and I've said goodbye to my car. For months we tried to sell it. It had only done 6000 miles and it was in mint condition, but nobody even made an offer. We ended up giving it to Joan's brother whose car was wrecked in a road accident. He gave us what he could afford and we let Jenny and Scott split the proceeds. It was a sad day when I watched him drive it away.

March 1993

It is Sunday, March 7th, and our fortieth wedding anniversary. I had to ask a neighbour to choose a card for me to give to Joan. Had I been well we would have been celebrating on a holiday abroad. As it is I am not even fit to take Joan out for a meal. Scott and his girlfriend come up to spend the weekend with us so Joan makes a celebration roast dinner. Halfway through the meal I have to leave the table to rest in an easy chair. It is a poor kind of anniversary and it's very unfair to Joan who has put up with me all these months.

I think back over the last forty years. I suppose I have never been what they call "a man's man", possibly because I've never been a drinker. Unlike many of my office colleagues, I didn't make a habit of flirting with the clerkesses nor of telling smutty jokes. I've always been happiest in mixed company. In general I find men, on their own, seem intent on trying to impress one another. I don't indulge in that kind of verbal one-upmanship. I valued the friendships I had with a few people, but over the years those friends with whom we spent such happy times are no longer around. Ralph and I have kept up a correspondence since he moved back to the States after Margaret died. Occasionally we see Enid and Dave but they now live on the south coast. The rest have died.

I am proud of Jenny and Scott, who have been so supportive since I have been ill. We seem to have exchanged roles. Once Joan and I looked after them and now they look after us. I most enjoyed being a dad to them when they were young, mending their toys, playing games with them and giving them treats. I cannot remember any promise that I ever made to them which went unkept. I didn't cope as well with them as they reached their teens. In the tiny photograph I carry in my wallet Jenny still has her pony-tail so she must have been about seven years old and Scott about four.

It has been difficult being a grandfather when I so rarely see Jenny's youngsters and have to content myself with buying the holiday ice creams. I harbour some regrets that I have been denied the pleasure which Joan enjoys as a grandparent. I think it is an age thing. I have lacked her energy to do the constant trips to keep in touch.

I think of Joan. I am very proud of my wife. If she had not gone back to teaching, which she loved, we would today have been living far less comfortably on my national insurance pension. The extra retirement contributions that I made have, over the years of inflation dwindled to a mere subsidy of less than twenty pounds per month.

I find that these days my mind constantly carries me back into the past, a sure sign that I'm living on "borrowed time". I have only to open my wardrobe to find there, along with the birthday and father's day cards which the children gave me over the years, the two little books and some of the letters that Joan sent to me in 1952. I keep them together beside the scribbled verses that Joan stayed up late to scribble for me to smile at on each birthday or anniversary.

I remember something she once said after a disagreement: "I find it very difficult to live with somebody who is always so cock-sure of himself." I was speechless for a moment before I said, very calmly and deliberately, "You are quite wrong about me. I have never been cock-sure, as you call it, about anything. I frequently question things that I've said and done. About some of these words and actions I have regrets with one exception. Not once in all our years together have I ever questioned or regretted my decision to ask you to be my wife. It was a bonus when that union was blessed with children. You made that possible. I hate to think what my life would have been like without you."

March 1962
For The Record
(The year Alex was promoted to "Control")

A happy anniversary, dear, for 1962.
It's quite a thought recalling all the years I've
    spent with you.
When I met an Alex Park back in the dim and
    distant past,
An up and coming salesman with some years
    before the mast,
How could I know that slim and boyish figure
    that I met
Would one day lead me in a whirl to join the
    upper set?
The father of my children I had planned to
    choose with care.
I didn't want them living on their mother and
    fresh air.
No fears need 1 have harboured for their precious
    little souls
Had I known their future father would be up
    with the "controls".
I've a honey of a hubby and I really must confess
I AM enjoying basking in the rays of his success.
Any moment now we will be emptying the till
And we'll soon be giving lifts to all the peasants
    up the hill.
With bricks and brains and growing pains we
    might look out and see
A garage standing one fine day ere 1963.

When we reach our silver wedding, I don't think
    there's any doubt
We'll remember 1962; the year the Parks stepped
    out!

October 1963
To the Last of the Forties

There's a wind that blows up some place but just
    where I can't recall.
I'm afraid the Geog. I learned at school was, well
    — was none at all.

It doesn't really matter as the forties I prefer
Are the ones since 1953 — the years we've had to
    share.

According to psychologists, who surely ought to
    know,
You should have upped and fled the nest at least
    five years ago.

Instead of which you've held your spleen in many
    a friendly fight,
And though I'd never own it, had me knowing
    you were right.

I don't have need to tell you that you're quite the
    nicest Dad
That two such darling menaces have ever ever
    had.

If in the time you've fathered them you've lost a
    bit more hair,
You can find some consolation owning such a
    handsome pair.

But just before I finish, 'cos today is almost
 through,
There surely is one thing to add before your
 birthday's due:

I love you now you're forty-nine and I will always
 be
So glad to know you chose to spend your forties
 all with me.

March 1965
On Our Twelfth

There's been time to get to know you and, as
  night must follow day,
To anticipate your actions, even forecast what
  you'll say.
There's "Joan, are you awake or not?" as
  Teasmade rings the bell.
There's "Let's be out for half-past eight" and
  "One can never tell!"
There's "Did you switch the fire off?" and "Have
  you got your key?"
And "Must this heater still be on?" and "Don't
  make tea for ME."
There's "Don't you think it's time, dear, you
  were cutting down the fags?"
And "Your Mummy's always tidy even though
  she's in her rags."
"Now, don't stay up till midnight!", "Joan, you're
  missing all the sun."
"Your hair looks very nice, dear. I forgot you'd
  had it done."
"I just dropped off that minute. What happened
  to his wife?"
"Now, THAT, I must confess I couldn't do to
  save my life."
"If you paid a man, he couldn't do a job as well
  as that."
"Well, if that is entertainment, I guess I'll eat my
  hat."

When you come to think about it, twelve years is
  quite a time
And, although I'm never short of words, I'm run-
  ning out of rhyme.
If you've not already guessed it, I suppose I'll
  have to tell —
It's all these dear familiar words which make life
  really swell.
The nicest are, "I love you." You can say them till
  you're hoarse
But by now I've learned to hear them in
"Oh good, you've made the sauce."

October 1965
From Me to You On Scoring Your Half Century

They say it took the Mastermind a paltry seven
days
To make a universe that's perfect in so very
many ways.
But the fractious human element that walks the
planet Earth
Falls short of the perfection that was all its right
by birth.
There's a tendency in humans to be always
giving in;
It's what the theologians call "the origin of sin".
For most it means we lack the will to see a job
right through.
I've found the one exception to the rule, dear;
Yes! It's you!
I've thought and thought, and having thought I
came to this conclusion:
There's nothing that YOU do by halves and this
is no illusion.
You're wholly loving, wholly kind and wholly
human too.
You've a smashing sense of humour and a grasp
of values true.
Oh, I don't pretend you're perfect, how could I
love a saint?
But, honey, I like what you are as well as what
you ain't.

But most of all I love you, 'cos you seem content
to be
The husband of a wife as unmethodical as me.
For most of us the Yesterdays are dreams we fear
will perish;
For most of us Tomorrow is a hope we vaguely
cherish.
But you and I have Yesterdays that time cannot
destroy
And ALREADY we are drinking from tomorrow's cup of joy.
So on the celebration of your two score years
and ten,
It's nice to know that someone thinks you quite
the best of men.
A Happy Birthday, darling! Though the words
are said in fun
And the thoughts appear so prejudiced, I mean
them — every one!

Some Birthday in the Seventies, I think.

I've been in half a dozen shops and looked at
many a rhyme
But none were truly ME to YOU what I wish at
this time.
I wish you health. I wish you strength to stay
awake at night,
But, just because it's you, dear — fall asleep. It's
still alright.
I wish you'd sit up half the night, I love a real
good natter,
But, just because it's you, dear, it doesn't really
matter.
I wish you had a partner who rose willingly from
bed
But, just because it's you, dear, I'm glad it's me
instead.
I wish you had the kind of kids who always toed
the line
But, just because it's you, dear, I'll own their
faults are mine.
I wish you had some hidden vice that only I
could find
So that, just because it's you, dear, I'd never even
mind.
I hope you'll stay just as you are in everything
you do
'Cos, just because you're you, dear, is why I married you.

March 1976

Remembering how, in '53,
You got around to marrying me.
It doesn't seem that long ago
That I was just a Miss Joan Lowe.
We did a lot in those first years
With many laughs and some odd tears,
Changing again the names we had.
Mine changed to "Mum" and yours to "Dad".
From telling stories, mending toys,
We moved to weighing up the boys,
And presently, with little pause,
We found that we were called "In Laws".
And now that we're reduced to three,
An "Upstairs, downstairs" family,
As son talks chiefly to the phone,
I wonder where the years have flown.
Sometimes, I think that, on the way
There hasn't been much time to say,
That knowing how you loved and cared,
Has made complete the joy we've shared
On this our anniversary.
When years we've shared are twenty three
No card could put it just as clearly.
"I love you very, very dearly."

October 1980
A Birthday Tribute to my Husband

With illustrations on each page the card said . . . *A shoulder to lean on, a wonderful mind, a smile that just sends me, a nice helping hand, a man in a million, just perfectly grand*. It became revised to . . .

That shoulder that's leaned on — now let us be
   fair,
It's MINE that YOU lean on when climbing the
   stair.
I can live without leaning but not without heat,
So you keep your shoulder but PLEASE warm
   my feet.

A wonderful mind! With that I'll agree
(Else how could you pick such a winner as me!).
It's brilliant, it's agile, gigantic and — wait,
It records every detail, remembers each date.
It copes with the letters and bills and big buys,
Not harassed by hatred nor laboured by lies.
Granted, land must lie fallow where later we reap
But 'tis sad that a genius needs so much sleep.

A smile that just sends me! Yes, right from the
   start
I admit it was YOUR smile which sizzled my
   heart,

And that hasn't changed, dear. You still wear a
   grin
When for what needs a needle I give you a pin,
When the tape that you ask for I just cannot
   find,
When the message you wanted has just slipped
   my mind.
It won't be your fault, dear, if one day the grin,
Like the hair and the patience, looks like wearing
   thin.

A nice helping hand! Well, you always give that,
Whether painting a door or re-binding mat,
Whether washing the dishes or cleaning the
   shoes,
Repairing the iron or mending a fuse.
I hope when you come to the end of this life
That heaven's reward is "A Practical Wife".

A man in a million, just perfectly grand!
Come hell or high water on that I will stand.
We get pretty near hell in the car when you say
"You can drive it yourself, if you want it that
   way."
And as for high water, well, this I have found —
With you still ashore I don't want to get
   drowned.
To a world full of women I'd leave you behind,
A poor sort of heaven that lacked peace of mind!

March 1984

The card said ***If I made a list of all
your good qualities where would I have room
left to say I Love You?***
This was added. . ..

But seeing there is all this space I thought I'd
   name a few
Of all the many ways you find of saying "I love
   you".
I am woken every morning with a welcome cup
   of tea,
And frequently my coffees are waiting here for
   me.
A chauffeur's at my beck and call, the car is
   always trim,
I name the destination and you meet my every
   whim.
A handyman I have at hand to mend and
   decorate
Who will even dust and vacuum to accommodate
   his mate.
The table's set, the spuds are peeled and all the
   dishes done.
I look around for jobs to do, you've done them
   every one.
I never touch the mower or the shears or hoe or
   spade,
I only move the deckchairs when I find them in
   the shade.

The ladies of the neighbourhood all envy me my
  spouse.
"If life were fair," they say, "There should be one
  in every house."
As my wrapper-up of parcels, as the clerk of all
  my post,
As my ever-handsome escort, as my very gracious
  host,
Among all the other husbands you rank as
  Everest
And every day in every way I know I've got THE
  BEST.

Also available in ISIS Large Print:

86 Smith Street

Joan Park

A memoir that recaptures ordinary family life in 1930s Britain

Daughter of a ship steward and a housewife, Joan Park gives a delightful glimpse of her childhood from 1927 to 1941, when she and her family lived at 86 Smith Street in Liverpool.

From the descriptions of her granddad's shoe repair shop to the stories her mother used to tell, Joan Park recounts her personal memories of the time of the Great Depression with a child's innocent eye. This is life as she encountered it in those days — family, friends, school and the little incidents — all of which had a big part to play in the day-to-day life of a little girl growing up in Liverpool.

ISBN 0-7531-9842-8 (hb)
ISBN 0-7531-9843-6 (pb)

After 86 Smith Street

Joan Park

The sequel to 86 Smith Street

Joan Park, the little girl of 86 Smith Street, takes us back to the early war years in this continuation of her memoirs. She is now fast growing up in a new housing estate on the outskirts of Liverpool and her world broadens to embrace a new baby in the family, new schools, new friends and a newly-emerging independence.

ISBN 0-7531-9898-3 (hb)
ISBN 0-7531-9899-1 (pb)